Issued under the authority of the Home Office (Fire Department)

Manual
Fireman

G000231671

A survey of the science of fire-fighting

Book 6
Breathing apparatus and resuscitation

London
Her Majesty's Stationery Office

ISBN 0 11 340586 3

Preface

It is not so many years ago that the criterion of a good fireman was considered by his colleagues to be his 'ability to eat smoke' and the use of breathing apparatus was the exception rather than the rule. In fact only a handful of firemen in a brigade were hand-picked and given special breathing apparatus training. They were then detailed to ride the emergency tender as a 'B A man' and went on to all special fires when breathing apparatus was requested.

Nowadays breathing apparatus is carried on all first-line appliances, and by virtue of the amount of plastics and other material to be found in upholstery, etc., which will produce masses of thick black smoke, even a fire in a small domestic dwelling can be a 'B A job'. Consequently all local authority firemen receive special training in the use of breathing apparatus almost as soon as they have completed their recruit's training.

As a result of deliberations by the Joint Training Committee of the Central Fire Brigades Advisory Council, a 'Breathing Apparatus Procedure' was introduced. This 'Procedure' must be instigated at any incident where breathing apparatus is worn. Furthermore, to overcome the difficulties of communication between breathing apparatus wearers inside premises and the B A Control which is set up outside the point of entry, special communication equipment has been devised.

In the past the description of breathing apparatus equipment and the control procedures have appeared in different volumes of the *Manual of Firemanship*. With the introduction of the new format for the *Manuals*, the subject of breathing apparatus has been collected into this one volume. Part 1 deals with the description of breathing apparatus and allied equipment, and Part 2 is concerned with the operational use of breathing apparatus. Because resuscitation and resuscitation equipment is a kindred subject, this is dealt with in Part 3.

Home Office
October 1973

Metrication

List of SI units for use in the fire service.

Quantity and basic or derived SI unit and symbol	Approved unit of measurement	Conversion factor
Length metre (m)	kilometre (km) metre (m) millimetre (mm)	1 mile = 1·609 km 1 yard = 0·914 m 1 foot = 0·305 m 1 inch = 25·4 mm
Area square metre (m²)	square kilometre (km²) square metre (m²) square millimetre (mm²)	1 mile² = 2·590 km² 1 yard² = 0·836 m² 1 foot² = 0·093 m² 1 inch² = 645·2 mm²
Volume cubic metre (m³)	cubic metre (m³) litre (l) (10⁻³m³)	1 cubic foot = 0·028 m³ 1 gallon = 4·546 litres
Volume, flow cubic metre per second (m³/s)	cubic metre per second (m³/s) litres per minute (l/min = 10⁻³m³/min)	1 foot³/s = 0·028 m³/s 1 gall/min = 4·546 1/min
Mass kilogram (kg)	kilogram (kg) tonne (t) = (10³ kg)	1 lb = 0·454 kg 1 ton = 1·016 t
Velocity metre per second (m/s)	metre/second (m/s) International knot (kn) kilometre/hour (km/h)	1 foot/second=0·305 m/s 1 UK knot = 1·853 km/h 1 Int. knot = 1·852 km/h 1 mile/hour = 1·61 km/h
Acceleration metre per second² (m/s²)	metre/second² (m/s²)	1 foot/second² = 0·305 m/s² 'g' = 9·81 m/s²

Quantity and basic or derived SI unit and symbol	Approved unit of measurement	Conversion factor
Force newton (N)	kilonewton (kN) newton (N)	1 ton force = 9·964 kN 1 lb force = 4·448 N
Energy, work joule (J) (= 1 Nm)	joule (J) kilojoule (kJ) kilowatt-hour (kWh)	1 British thermal unit = 1·055 kJ 1 foot lb force = 1·356 J
Power watt (W) (=1 J/s = 1 Nm/s)	kilowatt (kW) watt (W)	1 horsepower=0·746 kW 1 foot lb force/second = 1·356 W

Pressure
newton/metre^2 (N/m^2)
(= 1 Pascal (Pa))
	bar = 10^5 N/m^2
	millibar (m bar)
	  (= 10^2 N/m^2)
	metrehead
		1 atmosphere =
		   101·325 kN/m^2 =
		   1·013 bar
		1 lb force/in^2 =
		   6894·76 N/m^2=0·069 bar
		1 inch Hg = 33·86 m bar
		1 metrehead = 0·0981 bar
		1 foot head = 0·305
		   metrehead

Heat, quantity of heat joule (J)	joule (J) kilojoule (kJ)	1 British thermal unit = 1·055 kJ

Heat flow rate
watt (W)
	watt (W)
	kilowatt (kW)
		1 British thermal unit/
		   hour = 0·293 W
		1 British thermal unit/
		   second = 1·055 kW

Specific energy,
calorific value,
specific latent heat
joule/kilogram
  (J/kg)
joule/m^3 (J/m^3)
	kilojoule/kilogram
	  (kJ/kg)
	kilojoule/m^3 (kJ/m^3)
	megajoule/m^3 (MJ/m^3)
		1 British thermal unit/
		   lb = 2·326 kJ/kg
		1 British thermal
		unit/ft^3 = 37·26 kJ/m^3

Temperature degree Celsius (°C)	degree Celsius (°C)	1 degree centigrade = 1 degree Celsius

Contents

Part 1
Breathing apparatus equipment

Chapter 4 Oxygen breathing apparatus

Chapter 5 Compressed-air breathing apparatus

Chapter 6 Other breathing apparatus equipment

Chapter 7 Breathing apparatus cylinders

Chapter 8 Working duration of breathing apparatus

Part 2
The operational use of breathing apparatus

Chapter 9 Working with breathing apparatus

Chapter 14 Working in pressurised atmospheres

Part 3
Resuscitation

Chapter 15 Resuscitation

List of plates

Part 1
Breathing apparatus equipment

Poisonous atmospheres are among the many hazards which hinder the approach of firemen to extinguish a fire or to make a search of premises to find persons overcome or trapped because of heat and smoke. This has led to the development of a self-contained breathing apparatus which will enable the wearer to enter irrespirable atmospheres in safety and to work in them.

Part 1 of this volume describes the various types of oxygen and compressed-air self-contained breathing apparatus which are in use by fire brigades in this country, together with ancillary apparatus, such as air-line equipment, which may also be brought into service when the need arises.

Chapter 1
Elementary physiology of respiration

It is well known that if respiration ceases, either from an insufficiency of oxygen in the atmosphere, or from some physical cause which makes breathing impossible (such as pressure on the throat or chest), then life cannot be maintained. It is equally well known that special apparatus can be used to support life in conditions under which it would otherwise be impossible for a human being to breathe. In order to understand fully the principles which govern the use of this apparatus, however, it is first necessary to know something of the composition of the atmosphere and of the process of respiration itself.

Oxygen may be regarded as the most important of all foods, for all the energy of the body, warmth and life itself are dependent on the oxidation of foodstuffs in the body tissues. Oxygen is a constituent of the air, and air is normally taken into the body through the nose, the membranes of which besides warming and moistening the air, also act as a filter for extracting dust and germs.

When at rest the body requirements are comparatively low, and air is sucked into and out of the lungs by breathing movements at a rate of about 15 to 18 times per minute. When more energy is exerted either through work or nervous excitement, the breathing rate is increased and may be as much as 30 times a minute, or even more. As the bodily demand for air increases, the nasal passages become insufficient for the air required and the mouth is opened to allow the passage of a greater volume, as when panting through hard work.

At rest about $\frac{1}{2}$ litre (30 cubic inches) of air is normally inhaled at each breath and about the same quantity is exhaled; this amount is known as *tidal air*. By taking a very deep breath, a further 2 litres (120 cubic inches), known as the *inspiratory reserve volume*, may be taken in, making a total of about $2\frac{1}{2}$ litres (150 cubic inches) in all. On subsequent very deep exhalation, this may be increased by a further $1\frac{1}{2}$ litres (100 cubic inches), called the *expiratory reserve volume*, and the total exhalation is about 4 litres (250 cubic inches). The total amount thus exhaled is known as the *vital capacity* and varies with different people.

This variation in lung capacity is the reason for variation in the demands on breathing apparatus for different wearers doing the same work.

1 Composition of air

The atmosphere or air which is drawn into the lungs consists of three principal gases in the following proportions by volume:

	Per cent
Nitrogen	79
Oxygen	21
Carbon dioxide	Traces

It also contains small percentages of five other gases, such as argon, etc., but as these constitute a total of about 0·91 per cent of the atmosphere and, moreover, can only be separated from nitrogen with difficulty, it is usual for ordinary purposes to include them in the percentage of nitrogen.

The three main gases, nitrogen, oxygen and carbon dioxide, are readily separated, as they are not combined with each other. Whenever air is inhaled, therefore, nitrogen, oxygen and carbon dioxide are drawn into the body in the proportions indicated above.

The sustenance which the body requires from the air is derived from one of its constituents only, oxygen. Nitrogen takes no active part in respiration at ordinary pressures, being merely an inert gas which passes in and out of the body practically unchanged, whilst carbon dioxide, although it has a valuable function as a respiratory stimulant, is actually produced by the process of respiration in greater quantities than it is supplied by the atmosphere.

2 The function of oxygen in maintaining life

Breathing or respiration is a spontaneous action which unless some physical cause intervenes, is performed automatically by the human body some 15 to 30 times every minute from the moment of its birth to its death. The body performs this action because it needs oxygen, which is normally obtained only from the atmosphere. To obtain this, air must be drawn into the lungs, held for a sufficient time for the oxygen required to be absorbed and then expelled. This process is known as respiration, and consists of two physical actions, inhalation (breathing in) and exhalation (breathing out).

Inhalation is caused by the enlargement of the chest cavity, by which air is drawn into the lungs, and exhalation by the contraction of the chest cavity, which expels the air from the lungs. Inhalation is effected by a muscular effort which raises the ribs and at the same time lowers the diaphragm, thus increasing the capacity of the chest and creating a partial vacuum which causes the air to enter. Exhalation requires no muscular effort, as, when the breath is released, the ribs fall and the diaphragm rises of their own volition, thus lessening the capacity of the chest and forcing the air out.

The function performed by oxygen in maintaining life is extremely complicated and is difficult to describe without using medical phraseology. To put it in the simplest form possible—the body may be likened to a great number of small chemical engines each of which needs fuel and oxygen to keep it running, and an exhaust to carry away the fumes. Every time a muscle is used, whether for walking, sleeping, eating, breathing, or other bodily function, one of these engines is started and fuel and oxygen must be supplied to it. The fuel is provided by the digestive system and the oxygen by respiration. At the same time a quantity of carbon dioxide and other waste products is given off.

The transfer of the inhaled oxygen from the lungs to these engines, or in effect, to the muscles, is effected by the blood, which in its circuit of the body passes through the lungs, where it absorbs a certain quantity of oxygen. This oxygen travels with the blood through the main arteries to the lesser arteries, and finally into a vast network of blood vessels known as capillaries. These vessels have very thin walls through which a continual discharge of oxygen and assimilation of carbon dioxide takes place.

3 The composition of air after exhalation

As was explained above, carbon dioxide and other waste products are given off in this process and these are absorbed into the blood through the capillaries, the oxygen carried by the blood being given off at the same time. The blood, which has now changed from a bright to a dark red, is then driven back by the action of the heart to the lungs where the carbon dioxide is given off (and exhaled) and a further supply of oxygen is taken up.

In this process the composition of the air changes to approximately:

	Per cent
Nitrogen	79
Oxygen	17
Carbon dioxide	4

That is to say, about 4 per cent of oxygen is absorbed and an equal amount of carbon dioxide given off. There is often a slight increase in the percentage of nitrogen, derived from the waste products of nitrogenous foodstuffs which are assimilated by the blood at the same time as the carbon dioxide.

4 Breathing under varying degrees of effort

The amount of oxygen required by the body varies with the amount of work performed. If the body is resting, only the involuntary muscles governing the action of the lungs, the heart and the digestive organs are being used and consequently very little oxygen is required. As soon as the body becomes active, more muscles are used, a greater quantity of carbon dioxide is produced and a larger supply of oxygen is required.

Table 1 is compiled from a series of experiments undertaken by the late Professor J S Haldane, MB, FRS, and gives an indication of the variation in oxygen consumption and air respired for varying degrees of exertion.

Table 1

Degree of exertion	Oxygen consumed per minute in litres	Air breathed per minute in litres	Volume of air at each respiration in litres	Number of respirations per minute
Rest in bed	0·237	7·7	0·457	16·8
Rest, standing	0·328	10·4	0·612	17·1
Walking at 2 miles per hour	0·780	18·6	1·27	14·7
Walking at 3 miles per hour	1·065	24·8	1·53	16·2
Walking at 4 miles per hour	1·595	37·3	2·06	18·2
Walking at 5 miles per hour	2·543	60·9	3·14	19·5

Note—28·3 litres = 1 cu ft

In heavier work, such as ascending an incline or running, the oxygen consumed may amount to 3 litres per minute, while the volume of air breathed may reach over 100 litres per minute.

5 Irrespirable atmospheres

The fact that an atmosphere cannot safely be breathed will be due to one of two main causes: oxygen want, or the presence of a poison or irritant. Oxygen want may be due to disease, obstruction of the air passages, emotional excitement, etc. The latter, for example, causes some people to faint on hearing bad news, the shock of which causes a sudden demand for more oxygen than is immediately available. Nervous excitement as, for instance, when confronted with some unusual circumstance, causes an increased demand for oxygen and the breathing rate is automatically increased. In this connection, it is particularly important that firemen are emotionally stable, so that abnormal demands on any breathing apparatus they may be wearing are reduced to a minimum.

At fires, smoke of varying density with solid particles in suspension may cause inflammation of the lungs with the formation of sputum, which considerably affects breathing. In addition to oxygen deficiency caused by carbon dioxide, carbon monoxide may also be present. Many other gases may also be encountered, e.g. ammonia, hydrogen sulphide, sulphur dioxide, fumes from paint and other industrial processes, petrol fumes, etc.

For satisfactory functioning of the body, the air breathed must contain at least 20 per cent of oxygen and no poisonous gases, although 100 per cent of oxygen may be breathed for several hours without ill effects. Any other deviation, either by reducing the oxygen content or by the introduction of poisonous gases, will have an adverse effect on the body functions. Broadly, air with an oxygen content only a few per cent below the normal 20 per cent may cause headache and lassitude, and further reductions can produce loss of consciousness and death. Of the poisonous gases, one of the most dangerous is carbon monoxide. Its poisonous action is due to the fact that it has a great affinity for the red blood corpuscles, with which it forms what is known as *carboxy-haemoglobin*, the result being that the blood cannot take oxygen from the lungs. An atmosphere containing only about 0·1 per cent of carbon monoxide, if breathed for half an hour, will render about a quarter of the red blood corpuscles of the body incapable of functioning. Inhalation of the pure gas causes almost instantaneous unconsciousness.

It will be seen, therefore, that comparatively slight variations of the normal atmosphere, either by a reduction in the oxygen content or the introduction of a poisonous gas, can seriously affect the functioning of the human body. The effects vary from inability to focus or concentrate, to faintness, collapse and death. Oxygen deficiency cannot normally be detected, and while some gases such as ammonia or sulphur dioxide make their presence known by their pungent smell, others such as carbon monoxide have no smell. Unless suitable tests can be carried out for either oxygen deficiency or poison gases, persons operating in such atmospheres may be quickly overcome without realising that the atmosphere is other than normal.

When fire fighting, or on special services such as sewer rescues or finding a leakage of gas in some industrial plant, firemen may be required to work in atmospheres which are both oxygen-deficient and toxic. The concentration may be up to 100 per cent of a known or unknown gas, and the air entirely deficient of oxygen. To survive in such conditions firemen must be given equipment which will provide adequate protection and a supply of air or oxygen sufficient to meet all demands likely throughout the operation.

6 Effects of working in hot and humid atmospheres

It is well known that a man can stand working under hot conditions for longer if the atmosphere is dry than if it is humid.

Extensive tests have been carried out for the National Coal Board to establish the effect of heat and humidity on a man and the effects of temperature and moisture content in the air he breathes. As a result, information is available to mines rescue teams as to the permissible working times according to the prevailing temperature and humidity. The working times vary for men wearing compressed oxygen apparatus (as used by fire brigades but of 2 hours' duration) as compared with liquid air apparatus, and are slightly longer for the latter apparatus because it provides cooler and drier air for the wearer to breathe.

High humidity combined with high temperature is a condition which takes time to develop, and it can occur only where ventilation is negligible. It is therefore not likely to arise at fires except on very rare occasions. Nevertheless it is considered useful training for a breathing apparatus wearer to experience the effects of hot and humid conditions. Humidity plants have therefore been installed at some fire brigade breathing apparatus training centres. Further information about working in hot and humid atmospheres is given in Part 2, 'Operational use of breathing apparatus', page 106, *et seq.*

7 Effects of working in pressurised atmospheres

The human body is made to function at normal atmospheric pressure, and any marked increase or decrease of this pressure adversely affects it. During normal working firemen are unlikely to meet conditions where the ambient pressure varies sufficiently to cause ill effects. There may, however, be occasions when it is necessary for operations to be carried out in circumstances where the atmospheric pressure is artificially increased. The problems arising when firemen have to work in pressurised atmospheres are dealt with in Part 2, Chapter 14.

Chapter 2
Early types of breathing apparatus

1 The evolution of breathing apparatus

The function of breathing apparatus is to enable the wearer to work in an atmosphere which would not otherwise support life. The necessity of such an apparatus has long been appreciated, and primitive devices of various kinds were in use as long as 100 years years ago. The earliest types consisted of a muzzle fitting to the mouth with valves connected to which were tubes, the ends of which remained in the outer air. This type was used for a considerable period, in default of anything better, but suffered from the disadvantage that the energy required to overcome the friction of the air passing through the pipe had to be provided by the respiratory efforts of the wearer and breathing was consequently extremely difficult.

A more complex apparatus consisted of an airtight helmet and jacket of cowhide fitted with a hose-coupling to which air was pumped through delivery hose (Fig. 2.1). In this type the exhaled air

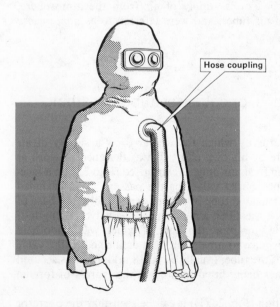

Hose coupling

Fig. 2.1 Smoke jacket respirator

9

escaped down under the skirt of the jacket and helped to keep the wearer cool in hot atmospheres.

A real attempt to master the problem was made in 1875 when Professor Tyndall, in conjunction with Sir Eyre Massey Shaw, devised and introduced a 'smoke cap', which was in fact the first respirator. This was similar in essentials to modern respirators, consisting of an airtight hood into which air was drawn from the atmosphere via a canister containing filtering elements.

All the early types of breathing apparatus were dependent upon a supply of oxygen from the atmosphere for their success. It was originally thought, from an insufficient understanding of the principles of respiration, that a respirator which would filter smoke and other gases would be effective under all conditions.

It was not realised that the greatest danger at a fire was due to oxygen deficiency, which nothing but a supplementary supply of air or oxygen could remedy. At least 16 per cent of oxygen is necessary to support life, and where due to combustion the percentage in the air is reduced below this figure, only apparatus which will provide its own supply of air (or oxygen) will enable the wearer to continue at work.

Apparatus depending on a self-contained supply of oxygen was produced for use in mines as early as 1881, but this type of breathing apparatus was not widely adopted for fire brigade use until after World War I.

The following are typical examples of early types of breathing apparatus which relied on a supply of air from the atmosphere, usually by means of air tubes, and were referred to as *atmospheric breathing apparatus*.

2 Short-distance, or equaliser-tube, breathing apparatus

This was an apparatus by which the wearer drew a supply of air from the atmosphere by his own effort. It was designed to work at a short distance from fresh air only. It comprised (Fig. 2.2(1)) a facepiece, with non-return outlet valve for the passage of the exhaled air and a flexible corrugated tube of rubber connected to the base of the facepiece to which was fitted a non-return inlet valve. A length of strong wire-embedded air pipe, the bore of which was smooth in order to reduce resistance to inhalation, was connected to the valve inlet. The free end of the tube, usually 60 ft (18 m) long, was secured in fresh air, a strainer being fitted to prevent the ingress of foreign matter.

From the illustration (Fig. 2.2(1)) it can be seen that the operator required no assistance when working in this apparatus, but it was of paramount importance that the free end of the pipeline was in fresh air, and a man was always left in attendance at the free end to ensure that it was not tampered with or moved into an impure atmosphere.

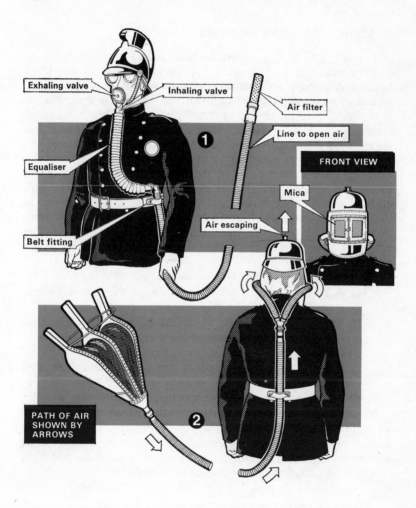

Fig. 2.2 (1) Equaliser tube breathing apparatus. (2) Bellows type smoke helmet

The disadvantages of this type of apparatus were:

    (a) The air tubing had to be trailed behind the wearer, thus restricting his movements to a certain extent and limiting the distance to which he could travel.

(b) The air tube could be cut or damaged by falling debris or other causes.

(c) The supply of air was dependent on the respiratory efforts of the wearer and involved considerable exertion.

3   Bellows smoke helmets

A popular type of this apparatus consisted of a simple headgear blocked out of hide which fitted over the head of the wearer, hood fashion. A piece of soft leather attached to the base of the helmet, tucked in under the wearer's tunic or coat, sealed the lower part of the helmet from surrounding air. Small clear mica windows in hinged frames giving a wide field of vision could be instantly opened and closed with a special locking device (Fig. 2.2(2)). Air entered the helmet by means of breathing tubes at each side of the helmet. An exhaling valve fitted on top of the helmet allowed the escape of excess and vitiated air. The air pipeline was non-collapsible, with embedded wire or armouring, and metal couplings. It was connected to a set of bellows which could be of pedal, hand, or sometimes power-operated type; this was situated in fresh air and with the efforts of a second person supplied a continuous flow of air to the wearer of the apparatus.

The disadvantages of this type of apparatus were:

(a) A constant supply of air was always dependent upon a second person.

(b) The air tubing had to be trailed behind the wearer, thus restricting his movements and limiting the distance he could travel.

(c) The air tubing could be cut or damaged by falling debris or other causes.

(d) The apparatus as a whole was bulky to stow.

More and more brigades discarded this type of apparatus in favour of 'self-contained' apparatus in which the wearer carried his own supply of air or oxygen. Nevertheless, despite the limitations of atmospheric types of breathing apparatus, their use continued on a diminishing scale until the beginning of World War II.

4   Self-contained self-generating breathing apparatus

This type of apparatus consisted of a respirator type of facepiece, breathing tube and canister. The canister was filled with chemicals (the peroxides of sodium and potassium) which both generated oxygen and absorbed carbon dioxide exhaled by the wearer. The warmth and moisture of the exhaled breath started the reaction, but this process took a little time. Other disadvantages were that the apparatus could not respond to a sudden demand for oxygen and, owing to the fact that the reaction of the peroxides was exothermic considerable heat was generated, which added to the discomfort of the wearer.

This type of apparatus was never widely used in this country, but it was developed and improved in the United States of America.

5 Self-contained oxygen breathing apparatus

The forerunner of the self-contained oxygen breathing apparatus now widely used in this country was introduced into fire brigades in about 1912. This apparatus was a development of that used in the mines and was of self-contained closed circuit type (Fig. 2.3). A

Fig. 2.3 Early type of self-contained oxygen breathing apparatus

cylinder of oxygen was carried sufficient for a duration of up to 1 hour. The exhaled breath was returned to a breathing bag containing an absorbent which removed the carbon dioxide; it was then mixed with a fresh supply of oxygen and used again. The wearer inhaled and exhaled through breathing tubes fitted with non-return valves and connected to a mouthpiece. Goggles were worn for protection of the eyes.

The carbon dioxide absorbent used in the early apparatus consisted of sticks of caustic soda, which assumed a brown sticky state in use. Later the caustic sticks were replaced by *coke soda*, a form of coke impregnated with caustic soda. Both these absorbents were difficult to remove from the bag, and it was essential to wash out the breathing bag with warm water after each time of use. Carbon dioxide absorbents of this type are no longer used in the United Kingdom, and have been replaced in modern breathing apparatus by a substance known as *soda lime* (*see* page 28).

In the closed circuit types of oxygen breathing apparatus no outside air is taken into the set, nor is the exhaled breath discharged to atmosphere. The exhaled breath is regenerated by removal of the CO_2 and the substitution of fresh oxygen, and the amount of oxygen to be carried is only that actually consumed by the wearer, so that the cylinder into which the oxygen is compressed (usually at a pressure of 120 or 132 atmospheres (bars)) is comparatively small.

From Table 1 it will be seen that to prevent a shortage of oxygen for a man walking at $3\frac{1}{2}$ miles per hour (5·6 km/h), a constant supply of 2 litres per minute should be available. This figure was the minimum provided in the early types of oxygen breathing apparatus, and is still the minimum provided in some modern types of apparatus referred to later.

The self-contained oxygen regenerative type of breathing apparatus gradually gained favour. Since some brigades preferred appliances using air to those supplying oxygen, the atmospheric types of apparatus died hard; their decline, however, was somewhat accelerated by the development of compressed-air apparatus, which appealed to those who retained a preference for air.

6 Self-contained air breathing apparatus

Various attempts were made to produce a breathing apparatus which carried its own supply of air as an alternative to the atmospheric types. One of the earliest made its appearance in about 1870. In this type, air was stored at atmospheric pressure in a bag carried on the back; the wearer inhaled from the bag and exhaled into it through a mouthpiece and breathing tubes. The intake was from the bottom of the bag where the air was cooler, and the exhaled breath was returned to the top. The air in the container quickly became deficient in oxygen, and the duration of the apparatus was only about 2–3 minutes. Fig. 2.4 is an illustration typical of this type of apparatus.

In about the middle 1920s the *Mandet* apparatus of French design came into use. The apparatus was self-contained, having air at high pressure stored in two cylinders carried on the wearer's back. The apparatus was marketed in this country by Messrs. Roberts, McLean and Co. Ltd. Later this firm developed their own set, on similar lines, which was known as the 'Roberts Compressed-Air Breathing Apparatus, Mark 41' (*see* page 68).

Fig. 2.4 Air breathing bag

The Mandet breathing set was of the open-circuit type in which the exhaled air is discharged into the atmosphere, and provision for a carbon dioxide absorbent is therefore unnecessary. It consisted of a respirator type of face mask with a breathing tube, and the two cylinders which discharged through a lung-governed demand valve. This valve operated according to the rate and depth of breathing and so provided the quantity of air demanded by the wearer.

The quantity of air carried in the two cylinders when fully charged was about 950 litres. From Table 1 it will be seen that a man walking at 4 miles per hour (6·4 km/h) breathes about 37 litres per minute. At this rate of work the apparatus had a nominal duration of about 25 minutes.

Chapter 3
Respirators

The knowledge that a face mask into which air was breathed through an absorbent filter in a container would support life under certain conditions led to the development of the filter-type respirator. Reference was made on page 10 to the early efforts of Professor Tyndall, but perhaps the great efforts in the development of respirators were made in securing protection against poison gas during World War II.

Respirators are designed to remove toxic substances and solid particles from the atmosphere before it is inhaled. This is done by some means of filtration, which may be either chemical or mechanical or a combination of both. Filter-type respirators consist of two or three essential parts according to type: the facepiece or mask, the connecting tube and the filter agent which is contained in a metal canister. The facepiece is usually of moulded rubber, with wide vision eyepieces, designed to make an effective seal on the face of the wearer, to which it is attached by means of an adjustable elastic head harness.

1 General Service respirators

Fig. 3.1 shows a filter respirator of the General Service type, which was issued to the fire service in World War II to meet the threat of gas warfare. These respirators were withdrawn after hostilities ceased. Some types of respirator dispense with the connecting tube, the filter canister being attached direct to the facepiece. Respirators issued for civilian use were of this type.

In addition to the development of respirators to meet the threat of chemical warfare, they have been developed for industrial use to give protection against certain known gases or groups of gases, dusts, paint fumes, etc. Those designed to give protection against gases have the canister marked with a distinctive colour, or combination of colours, to denote the particular gas against which they provide protection.

Respirators have a limited use in that they cannot be used in an atmosphere having insufficient oxygen to support life. They are not therefore, used by fire brigades in this country for general fire fighting, where reliance for protection is placed entirely on the self-contained types of breathing apparatus.

Fig. 3.1 Respirator as issued to the National Fire Service

2 Service respirators, type AG Mark 6 (light)

An issue has, however, been made to fire brigades of respirators for the express purpose of protection against the inhalation of radioactive dust in the open air, where the number of breathing apparatus sets immediately available is insufficient to meet the demand. The type of respirator at present available for this purpose is a Service pattern, type AG Mark 6 (light) (Fig. 3.2), which consists of a moulded rubber facepiece with glass eyepieces, head harness, an exhaling valve and a filter canister which is fitted with a non-return valve. The canister contains the filter materials, which do not deteriorate with time and will remain serviceable for many hours when the respirator is being worn.

These respirators afford complete protection to eyes, nose, throat and lungs against chemical warfare agents, biological warfare agents and radioactive dust, provided the respirator is properly fitted and is in serviceable condition. They do **not** provide protection against carbon monoxide, or oxygen deficiency, and should not be used for fire-fighting purposes other than in the conditions for which they are supplied. While in time dense smoke may cause some clogging of

17

the filter it would, if at all serious, become apparent to the wearer through a gradual increase in the breathing resistance. However, even in the worst conditions, a respirator will remain usable in smoke for a considerable time, certainly for several hours.

Moisture does not affect the protection given by these respirators, but resistance to breathing will increase if the filter becomes wet. Moisture can, however, cause some deterioration in storage, and after use at a fire a respirator should be properly dry before being returned to its haversack.

Fig. 3.2 Service pattern respirator, type AG Mark 6 (light), issued for protection against the inhalation of radioactive dust in the open air where breathing apparatus sets are not available

3 Care and maintenance of respirators

Respirators should be kept dry and away from any excessive heat; they should not be stowed underneath other equipment nor hung up by their harness elastics. Respirator haversacks should not be used to carry any items other than respirators and their associated equipment. Each respirator should be examined and tested at least once every six months. The examination should ensure that the facepiece, harness elastics and valves are in good condition and show no signs of perishing, and that the eyepiece and container wirings are secure.

The containers should be checked to see that they are not dented and have not been affected by water and that the threads are undamaged. Before valves are tested, a person should don the respirator and adjust it correctly by means of the straps. (It cannot be too strongly emphasised that correct fitting is vital for the effectiveness of any respirator.)

a. Testing

The procedure for testing is as follows:

(1) Inlet valve

Remove the canister. Close the outlet valve by holding a pad of cloth firmly over the valve guard. Holding the fingers over the inlet valve, the wearer should exhale forcefully. If the valve is functioning correctly, the air will be forced out between the edge of the facepiece and the face. If not, air will be felt coming over the fingers from the inlet valve assembly.

(2) Outlet valve

Place the fleshy part of the base of the thumb over the canister inlet hole whilst the wearer attempts to inhale. Provided the facepiece has been correctly fitted and the outlet valve is functioning, no air should enter the facepiece.

At each inspection respirators should be allowed to remain out of their haversacks for about half an hour to allow facepieces to resume their normal shape.

b. Cleaning

Respirators should be cleaned immediately after use and also at the time of the routine inspection. The cleaning procedure should be carried out as follows:

(1) Remove the canister.

(2) Turn back the head harness until it is supported on the outside of the facepiece.

(3) Turn the facepiece inside out to expose the interior of the facepiece, including the inlet valve and the air guide.

(4) Raise the inlet valve carefully by drawing back gently with a finger, and wipe the underside of the valve and seating with a damp cloth.

(5) Wipe and dry the inside of the facepiece with a cloth soaked in disinfectant (*see* section (c), page 20).

(6) Clean the eyepieces with the cloth supplied with the anti-dimming outfit and apply anti-dimming compound.

(7) Wipe the outskirts of the facepiece clean. If the head harness or the haversack is wet or muddy, allow it to dry and then brush.

(8) After drying, return the facepiece to normal.

(9) Replace the canister.

It is important that a probe is **not** used to dislodge mud or foreign bodies from the outlet valve assembly and/or speech transmitter, if fitted. If these cannot be removed by pouring clean water through the assembly, the respirator should be declared unserviceable.

c. Disinfecting

When disinfecting is considered necessary (e.g. for medical reasons) the following procedure should be followed:

(1) Detach the canister and ensure that the equalising pressure valve is closed. Immerse the whole of the facepiece in the disinfectant solution.

(2) After 5 minutes remove the facepiece and rinse well in cold water.

(3) Shake well to remove all moisture, particularly from the valve holder.

(4) Wipe with a clean dry rag and allow to dry naturally. Do not hang the respirator up by the head harness or turn it inside out. Do not apply heat whilst drying.

(5) Wipe the neck of the canister with a cloth moistened with the disinfectant solution, taking care that no fluid enters the canister.

(6) When the facepiece is dry, replace the canister and check that the outlet valve functions properly.

Disinfectants normally used for breathing apparatus face masks (*see* page 75) are also suitable for these respirators.

Chapter 4
Oxygen breathing apparatus

As indicated earlier in Chapter 2 oxygen breathing apparatus has been in use in fire brigades in this country since about 1912, and compressed-air sets since about 1925. Although atmospheric types of breathing apparatus were still in use in industry it became generally acknowledged that the only suitable breathing apparatus for fire brigade use was the self-contained type with its own supply of oxygen or air to give protection against any known or unknown gas. Accordingly self-contained oxygen and compressed-air sets gradually displaced all types of atmospheric breathing apparatus, and early in the life of the National Fire Service the few remaining atmospheric sets were replaced by self-contained apparatus. The 1-hour self-contained oxygen apparatus became the most widely used.

In this chapter oxygen breathing apparatus as used by fire brigades is described and this is followed in Chapter 5 by compressed-air sets. Reference is not necessarily made to each 'mark', or new model, of each type of set in current use, as the manufacturers generally provide adequate descriptions and instructions on the use and testing of their apparatus in their instruction books. Further, in some cases the basic design of the various types has not altered greatly over the years, the general principles remaining the same, and successive 'marks' have not provided any radical changes. However, in circumstances where there is a substantial difference between one 'mark' and another, details are given.

1 Specifications

In 1952 a requirement specification for self-contained breathing apparatus for fire brigade use was prepared by the Joint Committee on Design and Development of Appliances and Equipment, a committee of the Central Fire Brigades Advisory Council (England and Wales) and the Scottish Central Fire Brigades Advisory Council. The specification, JCDD/19, defines the term 'breathing apparatus' as an entirely self-contained apparatus which may carry cylinders containing compressed oxygen or air.

Three types of apparatus are covered by the specification:

(1) oxygen, closed circuit, using a *reducing* valve (constant predetermined flow);

(2) oxygen, closed circuit, using a *demand* valve (with or without a reducing valve); and

(3) compressed air, open circuit, using a *demand* valve.

21

All the apparatus described in the following paragraphs comply with the requirements of the specification, except the *Minox* in which the pressure reducer is not a constant flow type (*see* page 39).

British Standard (BS 4667) has been prepared for closed-circuit breathing apparatus (Part 1), open-circuit breathing apparatus (Part 2) and fresh air hose and compressed air-line breathing apparatus (Part 3). There is an associated British Standard (BS 4275) which contains recommendations for the selection, use and maintenance of respiratory protective equipment. These standards are expected in due course to supersede JCDD/19.

2 Self-contained oxygen breathing apparatus

One manufacturer, Siebe Gorman, produces two types of closed-circuit oxygen breathing apparatus which are in current use by fire brigades. Both are of the closed-circuit regenerative type, i.e. the carbon dioxide in the exhaled breath is removed by an absorbent and is replaced by fresh oxygen. Both sets have a nominal duration of 1 hour. These sets are (*a*) the *Proto*, which uses a reducing valve giving a constant predetermined flow and is the more generally used of the two, and (*b*) the *Minox*, a more recently introduced apparatus incorporating several unique features, but which so far is not widely used by fire brigades. The most outstanding feature of this set is the replacement of a constant flow reducing valve with a special flow control unit.

A feature of the closed-circuit apparatus is that the supply of oxygen for regeneration purposes is controlled to give a predetermined amount per minute, irrespective of the energy expended, and the duration of the supply is therefore known.

In sets of the closed-circuit type, therefore, the working time can be predetermined within fairly exact limits, which will vary according to the use of the by-pass which is incorporated to make good any temporary shortage of oxygen due to sudden great exertion.

If the supply of oxygen is regulated so that a given amount flows per minute irrespective of the energy consumed, then a breathing bag or other container must be provided in which a reserve can be built up, and the exhaled air must be returned to this reserve. Since the exhaled air will contain a percentage of carbon dioxide it follows that a means must also be provided for absorbing this gas so that the air is purified before being re-inhaled. Sets employing a circuit of this sort are known as the closed-circuit regenerative type.

The circuit employed by this type of apparatus is shown in diagrammatic form in Fig. 4.1. A cooler is not an essential feature, but is a desirable addition as a certain amount of heat is generated in the circuit. This circuit from the breathing bag to the mouthpiece and back in an endless circle is common to all types of regenerative apparatus.

The high pressure of the oxygen in the cylinder has to be reduced before the oxygen can safely be fed into the breathing circuit, and a means of reducing pressure is an essential feature of all breathing apparatus employing compressed gases. This may be done by a pressure-reducing valve which in some types of apparatus is augmented by a demand valve operated by the breathing action of the wearer.

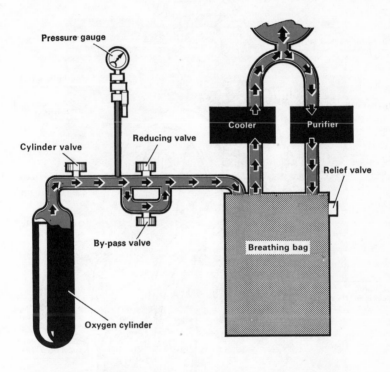

Fig. 4.1 Diagrammatic sketch showing the layout of closed-circuit regenerative apparatus

3 The *Proto* Mark V breathing apparatus

The oxygen breathing apparatus most commonly employed for fire brigade work is the *Proto*, a closed-circuit set having a nominal duration of 1 hour which uses a constant predetermined flow reducing valve. A diagrammatic view of the apparatus is shown in Fig. 4.2.

23

a. Description of the set

In the following description of the set, the various items are numbered in the same sequence as the numbers in Fig. 4.2.

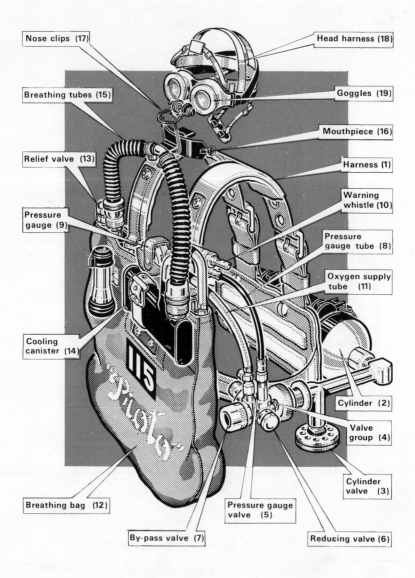

Nose clips (17)

Head harness (18)

Breathing tubes (15)

Goggles (19)

Mouthpiece (16)

Relief valve (13)

Harness (1)

Warning whistle (10)

Pressure gauge (9)

Pressure gauge tube (8)

Oxygen supply tube (11)

Cooling canister (14)

Cylinder (2)

Valve group (4)

Breathing bag (12)

Cylinder valve (3)

By-pass valve (7)

Pressure gauge valve (5)

Reducing valve (6)

Fig. 4.2 Diagrammatic view of the *Proto* Mark V breathing apparatus

(1) The harness

The apparatus is carried in a lightweight terylene harness placed over the shoulders of the wearer. The front part, which is carried on the chest, supports and gives protection to the rubber breathing bag. A small leather pouch protects the pressure gauge from damage and retains it in a readily accessible position for periodic inspection by the wearer during operations. The rear part of the harness is worn on the back and supports the oxygen cylinder which is secured by two quick-release metal bands. The cylinder arm brings the valve group to a position on the wearer's left side where the valves may be easily manipulated. To restrict the movement of the apparatus when worn, a body belt and complementary strap are provided, each with buckle-type fasteners.

When worn, the apparatus is well balanced and weighs without ancillary equipment approximately 27 lb (12·2 kg).

(2) Cylinder

The cylinder is made in three parts—body, arm and cylinder valve. These three parts are assembled during manufacture and are not normally dismantled. The cylinder valve is part of the cylinder arm and incorporates a fibre or hard plastic seating. An anti-rust tube is fitted in the cylinder body to arrest any small particles of rust and prevent them from passing into the valve group. The cylinder capacity is 6·6 cubic feet (187 litres) of medical oxygen compressed to a pressure of 1980 lbf/in² (132 atmospheres).* The cylinder is painted black with white shoulders and neck to denote that it contains medical oxygen.

(3) Cylinder valve

The gunmetal body of the cylinder valve is screwed securely to the outlet of the cylinder arm. The operating components, including the fibre or hard plastic seated valve, fit into the valve body. The valve is operated by a small handwheel which is turned in an anticlockwise direction to open. Under normal working conditions the cylinder valve should be kept in the fully-open position at all times.

---

* It is usual to convert lbf/in² to atmospheres by assuming 15 lbf/in² to equal 1 atmosphere, although a more accurate conversion factor would be 14·7 lbf/in²· The discrepancy involved is small (2 per cent) and is within the overall accuracy of B A gauges. It is on this basis that 1800 lbf/in² has been regarded as 120 atmospheres, 1980 lbf/in² as 132 atmospheres and 3000 lbf/in² as 200 atmospheres. As bars are introduced as the unit of pressure, a 'bar' may be regarded as equivalent to an 'atmosphere'. While existing gauges remain in use, the error involved will, of course, remain unchanged (2 per cent), but where new gauges are supplied scaled in bars, the discrepancy will be slightly increased to about 3·5 per cent, since 1 bar is equal to only 14·5 lbf/in². However, even this larger discrepancy is regarded as acceptable having regard to the accuracy of gauges.

(4) Valve group

Attached to the cylinder arm by means of the main union is the valve group. The main union is a large serrated threaded female connector which connects on to the mating outlet of the cylinder valve. A projecting hexagonal spigot in the valve group fits into a similarly shaped recess provided in the cylinder valve outlet. This ensures the correct positioning of the valve group in relation to the cylinder and prevents movement when connected. The union is a pneumatic one requiring only hand pressure to effectively tighten. Gas tightness is effected by a small neoprene 'O' ring which fits into a small groove on the spigot. A small sintered metal filter plug prevents dust and foreign matter from entering the central column of the valve group.

The valve group is composed of three valves:
  (i) pressure gauge valve;
  (ii) reducing valve;
  (iii) by-pass valve.

(5) Pressure gauge valve

Under normal operational conditions the pressure gauge valve remains open. It is fitted as a safety device and is intended to be used in an emergency only to isolate the pressure gauge, warning whistle and pressure gauge tube when some defect or fracture causes a serious oxygen leak. In such circumstances the valve must be immediately closed in order to conserve the oxygen supply. It is lever-operated, requiring only a quarter-turn to close (*see* Fig. 4.6).

(6) Reducing valve

As its name suggests this valve reduces the high-pressure oxygen delivered from the cylinder to a lower breathable pressure. It is set to deliver 2·5 litres per minute throughout the full duration of the set and works automatically, requiring no attention from the wearer. The operation of the reducing valve is described in section (b) (page 32).

(7) By-pass valve

The by-pass valve is an emergency valve which when operated supplies the wearer with an immediate additional supply of oxygen, e.g. when because of strenuous work the wearer finds that 2·5 litres of oxygen per minute provided by the reducing valve is insufficient for his requirements, or in the event of the oxygen supply being reduced or cut off due to a defect in the reducing valve. The by-pass valve is also used in the 'starting-up' procedure to fill the breathing bag, or during operational use as a means of replacing the warm exhaled breath of the wearer by flushing the bag with cool oxygen direct from the cylinder. It is press-button operated and must always be used with discretion. Incorrect or careless use may seriously reduce the duration of the set.

(8) Pressure gauge tube

A pressure gauge tube from the pressure gauge valve to the low-cylinder-pressure warning whistle and pressure gauge is provided to bring the gauge to an easily readable position. It is made of stout flexible 'techalon' tubing, approximately 18 ins (460 mm) long. Both ends are fitted with female connections; that which fits to the reducing valve has a metal-to-metal seating and the end connected to the low-cylinder-pressure warning whistle is fitted with a fibre washer.

(9) Pressure gauge

The pressure gauge is of the bourdon tube type and is calibrated in atmospheres and minutes. Each division represents 10 atmospheres or 5 minutes. A red line at 120 atmospheres indicates 60 minutes duration.

(10) Low-cylinder-pressure warning whistle

The low-cylinder-pressure warning whistle is fitted between the pressure gauge and the pressure gauge tube and is pre-set to actuate when the cylinder pressure drops to 30 atmospheres (15 minutes) or below. It sounds automatically and continuously to warn the wearer that it is time to withdraw to fresh air (*see* Chapter 10 on the 'Operational Procedure for the use of breathing apparatus'). In doing so the whistle consumes approximately 2 litres of oxygen per minute. This means that the safety margin of the set is cut from 15 minutes to approximately 10 minutes.

(11) Oxygen supply tube

This tube leads from the low-pressure side of the valve group to the oxygen inlet connection on the breathing bag. It is made of non-kink flexible rubber and has female connections at each end. The valve group connection is a metal-to-metal one and the breathing bag connection is fitted with a fibre washer. To prevent it catching on projections when the set is worn, the tube is looped around the goose-neck of the cooling canister before connection with the breathing bag.

(12) Breathing bag

The breathing bag (Fig. 4.3) is constructed of strong vulcanised indiarubber. It is divided into two compartments by a rubber curtain crossing diagonally from front to rear and extends from the top to within about 1 in (25 mm) of the bottom. To prevent complete deflation of the bag, $\frac{1}{4}$-in (6 mm) square rubber ribs are fitted internally, front and rear. At the top of the bag two moulded rubber blocks, which are stuck in position, hold four metal connections, two at each side. Those on the wearer's left are for connecting to the oxygen supply tube and to the cooling canister; both communicate with the rear compartment. The connections on the right are for the exhaling and relief valves respectively; these communicate with the front compartment.

The breathing bag is charged with $3\frac{1}{2}$ lb (1·6 kg) of granulated soda-lime absorbent (*Protosorb*), which is divided equally between the front and rear compartments and occupies the space in the

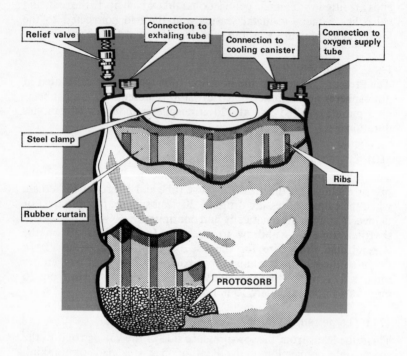

Fig. 4.3 The *Proto* Mark V breathing bag

bottom of the bag to a depth of about 3 ins (76 mm). This more than covers the communicating space at the foot of the curtain, between the front and rear compartments, and ensures that any gas moving from front to rear compartments must pass through the absorbent. To prevent undue movement of the absorbent when the wearer is working in awkward positions, e.g. on his side, the bag is 'waisted' about 6 ins (152 mm) from the bottom. This helps to contain the absorbent.

A small diffuser is fitted on the oxygen inlet inside the bag for the purpose of diffusing the oxygen delivered to the bag from the oxygen supply tube. This spreads the blast of high-pressure oxygen when the by-pass valve is used and prevents the disturbance of *Protosorb* dust which might cause discomfort to the wearer. The opening at the top of the bag enables the absorbent charge to be replaced; this opening is closed by two clamps and a rubber washer, the whole being kept gastight by wing nuts. Attachments to support the bag are provided on the wing nuts.

(13) Relief valve

When the wearer's oxygen consumption is less than the 2·5 litres per minute provided by the set, the bag becomes overfilled and consequently breathing is difficult. The relief valve at the top of the bag enables the wearer to discharge surplus oxygen from the bag to atmosphere. It is a small mushroom type valve which is operated manually.

As an alternative to the manual-type relief valve, an automatic type may be supplied with the set. This valve operates automatically when the pressure of oxygen in the breathing bag reaches a predetermined level. This type of valve is recommended for use with sets fitted with certain types of face mask.

(14) Cooling canister

The cooling canister (Fig. 4.4) is fitted between the breathing bag and inhaling valve and is designed to cool the oxygen immediately

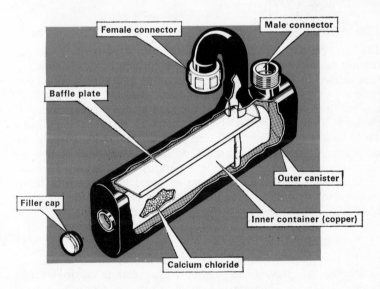

Female connector

Male connector

Baffle plate

Outer canister

Filler cap

Inner container (copper)

Calcium chloride

Fig. 4.4 Cooling canister fitted to the *Proto* set

before inhalation by the wearer. It consists basically of two canisters, one inside the other. The small inner one contains the chemical cooling agent – approximately 10 oz (283 g) of calcium chloride – which at normal temperature is in crystalline form. As the oxygen

29

passes into the larger outer canister and circulates round the smaller container, cooling is achieved by means of radiation and by the latent heat of fusion of the calcium chloride, which liquefies at 30°C. The charge does not deteriorate with use and in maintenance requires only topping up. After a set has been used, cold water should be circulated through the cooler for a short time to restore the chemical to its crystalline form.

(15) Breathing tubes and valves

The 1-in (25 mm) diameter breathing tubes are 9 ins (228 mm) in length; they are corrugated to provide flexibility and a certain amount of elasticity, and to prevent collapse of the tubes, ensuring the wearer of an adequate supply of oxygen at all times.

Spring-loaded mica non-return valves are fitted at the lower ends of the tubes. On inhalation, both valves lift, the inhaling valve opening and the exhaling valve closing. On exhalation the action is reversed, the inhaling valve closes and the exhaling valve opens. In this way, oxygen circulating in the set travels in one direction only. Mica is used in the manufacture of these valves because it is light in weight, it is unaffected by heat, and moisture does not affect the movement of the valve.

(16) Mouthpiece

The mouthpiece is soft vulcanised rubber, fitted to a 'Y'-shaped tubular connection-piece to which the breathing tubes are attached. It is shaped to fit comfortably between lips and gums and is completely gastight when properly adjusted. The two rubber nipples projecting from the inner part of the mouthpiece prevent closing of the teeth. Two, or alternatively four, metal 'D' rings enable the outer flange of the mouthpiece to be secured to the hooks of the head-hardness. A nylon plug is supplied with the mouthpiece so that the aperture may be sealed when the apparatus is not in use. This prevents dust and carbon dioxide from the atmosphere entering the set and causing deterioration of the absorbent charge in the breathing bag.

(17) Nose clips

Spring nose clips are supplied to be used in conjunction with the mouthpiece to prevent the wearer from inhaling noxious fumes through the nose. They are adjustable to suit any nose.

(18) Head-harness

The head-harness is made from a light but sturdy plastics material, and is designed rather like a scrum-cap. It is readily adjusted to suit the wearer and short straps with hooked ends connect with the 'D' rings of the mouthpiece supporting it in the correct position. The light nature of the strapping enables a fire helmet to be worn without discomfort.

(19) Goggles

Protection for the eyes is afforded against smoke and irritant gases by the use of goggles. The frames are made of soft moulded rubber and the eyepieces are non-splinter. The goggles are held in position by a quick-adjusting elastic head-band. Eyepieces should be treated on the inside with anti-mist preparation to prevent condensation during use.

(20) Face masks

Face masks of the full vision type (Fig. 4.5) are gaining in popularity as an alternative to mouthpieces, nose clips and goggles. The great advantage of the mask is that it can be provided with a special diaphragm which makes it possible for wearers to converse normally

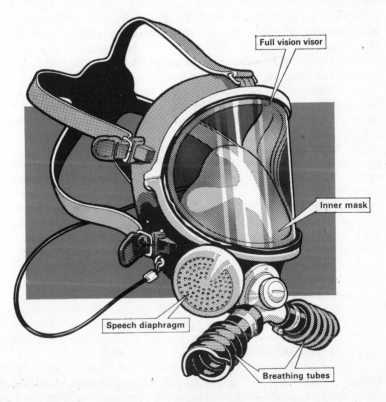

Fig. 4.5 Full vision face mask for use with *Proto* breathing apparatus

with one another. It is not possible to articulate when a mouthpiece
is worn, and any tendency for a wearer to 'talk round a mouthpiece'
is a practice which should be avoided. It could have serious consequences in strong concentrations of carbon monoxide.

The mask is of the wide vision type and is made of moulded
rubber. It incorporates a pneumatic seal at the sealing edge of the
mask which can be adjusted to suit the wearer. The head-harness
for the mask consists of five straps, the top one being permanently
attached, while the remaining four rubber straps are adjustable and
retained by quick-release buckles.

When face masks are used instead of mouthpieces the breathing
tubes are attached to the mask by means of a metal 'Y' connection.
Further information about face masks is given in Chapter 5 in
connection with compressed-air apparatus.

b. Action of the reducing valve

Oxygen enters the reducing valve (Fig. 4.6) at the main union, passes
through the small sintered bronze filter (1) and makes its way along
the central column (2). It escapes through the inlet jet (3), which is
set at right angles to the central column, and begins to fill the upper
half of the reducing valve (i.e. the space above the rubber diaphragm
(4)). Further progress is checked by the back-pressure disc (5),
the 0·013 in (0·33 mm) diameter orifice which allows only a limited
amount of oyxgen to escape to the low-pressure side of the set.

As a result of the restriction to the flow caused by the back-
pressure disc, a back pressure builds up in the upper half of the
reducing valve. When it has reached sufficiently high proportions
(about 2 atmospheres), this back pressure, acting on the large area
of the diaphragm, forces the diaphragm with all its attached components in a downward direction, thus slightly compressing the
spiral spring (6) and causing the floating valve seating (7) to baffle
the inlet jet, thereby restricting the flow of oxygen from the central
column. The leak of oxygen through the small hole in the back-
pressure disc reduces the pressure against the diaphragm and the
spiral spring is able to re-assert itself, so that the diaphragm and
floating valve components are returned to their original position,
thus uncovering the main jet again and allowing the flow of high-
pressure oxygen to recommence.

It may appear from this description of the action of the reducing
valve that the diaphragm and attached components vibrate continually while the oxygen flow is maintained, but this is not the case.
What actually happens is that the floating valve adopts a position
(usually from 0·001 to 0·002 in (0·025 to 0·05 mm) above the inlet
jet) related to the pressure of oxygen delivered from the cylinder.
Initially, when the pressure is high (132 atmospheres) the floating
valve is very near the inlet jet, but as the pressure of oxygen dimi-
nishes, the floating valve moves progressively farther away from the

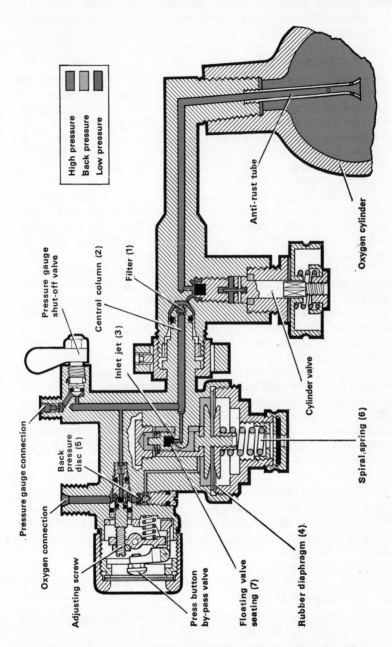

High pressure
Back pressure
Low pressure

Pressure gauge shut-off valve

Central column (2)

Filter (1)

Inlet jet (3)

Pressure gauge connection

Oxygen connection

Back pressure disc (5)

Adjusting screw

Press button by-pass valve

Floating valve seating (7)

Rubber diaphragm (4)

Spiral spring (6)

Cylinder valve

Oxygen cylinder

Anti-rust tube

Fig. 4.6 Diagrammatic arrangement of the *Proto* Mark V reducing valve

33

inlet jet until, when the cylinder pressure is approximately zero, it has returned to the starting position with the spiral spring fully extended.

c. Circulation of oxygen

When the cylinder valve is opened, oxygen flows from the cylinder through the main union and filter screw into the valve group. The pressure gauge valve being open, oxygen makes its way into the pressure gauge tube and on to the low-cylinder-pressure warning whistle and the pressure gauge. The whistle sounds momentarily as the pressure builds up to 30 atmospheres and ceases immediately this pressure is exceeded. The oxygen pressure in the central column is indicated by the pressure gauge.

In passing through the reducing valve, the high-pressure oxygen is reduced to a lower breathable pressure and the flow is regulated to 2·5 litres per minute. From the reducing valve outlet, the low-pressure oxygen enters the oxygen supply tube and passes into the rear compartment of the breathing bag via the small diffuser.

When the wearer inhales, oxygen from the rear compartment of the breathing bag is drawn into the cooling canister and after circulating round the inner container passes through the inhaling non-return valve into the inhaling tube and mouthpiece to the wearer's lungs. The exhaled impure breath enters the front compartment of the bag via the exhaling tube and non-return valve. Here it halts momentarily until the next inhalation, when it is drawn from the front compartment to the rear through the space below the rubber curtain (or diaphragm) between the two compartments of the bag. Whilst passing through the *Protosorb* absorbent charge, the carbon dioxide is removed and the gas diffuses into the rear compartment. Replenished with oxygen delivered by the cylinder through the reducing valve, the purified exhaled breath in the rear compartment is then re-inhaled.

d. Putting on the apparatus

It is important that the correct sequence of operations is followed when putting on and starting up the set, and the drill (Drill M3) as laid down in the *Fire Service Drill Book* should be carefully followed. When the set has been put on and adjusted properly, it should fit as shown in Fig. 4.7.

e. Operation of the set

If an oxygen breathing apparatus of the type described above has been correctly assembled and put on it will call for little further attention, and the wearer can safely leave it to its own business. The only items which need to be remembered are:

(1) The pressure gauge should be consulted from time to time to

Fig. 4.7 *Proto* apparatus correctly fitted on wearer

see how much oxygen remains in the cylinder, and therefore how long the wearer can remain in a poisonous atmosphere. The scale is calibrated in atmospheres and sometimes also in minutes. The lower end of the scale is usually marked in red to indicate when the wearer should withdraw to fresh air. In any event withdrawal should always be made as soon as the low-cylinder-pressure warning whistle sounds (*see* Chapter 10, 'Operational use of breathing apparatus').

The gauge will show a reading throughout the period when the set is in operation and if consulted at regular intervals will keep the wearer informed of the amount of oxygen left in the cylinder. As explained above, the pressure gauge valve is provided solely to prevent leakage of oxygen should the gauge or its flexible tube become damaged. It should never otherwise be closed.

(2) When a set other than the Mark V, which is fitted with an automatic relief valve, has been in use for some time, particularly if no strenuous work has been undertaken, the bag will be found to become unduly inflated and some of the excess contents should be released by means of the relief valve.

The fact that the bag inflates so much as to become obtrusive is in itself a sufficient reminder that the relief valve should be used. Breathing will also be found to become slightly uncomfortable if the bag is too full as the wearer will be exhaling against pressure; this should be regarded as a warning to use the relief valve.

(3) If the wearer is working under exceptionally arduous conditions, or indulging in short periods of violent effort, the regulated supply of 2·5 litres per minute may temporarily be insufficient for his needs, and a feeling of restriction may be experienced. When this occurs the by-pass valve should be opened momentarily to give an increased supply. It will also be found beneficial after working in a heated atmosphere for some time to discharge the accumulated gases in the breathing bag by using the relief valve, and to flush out the bag with a fresh supply of oxygen from the by-pass valve.

The by-pass valve serves also as a secondary means of supplying oxygen to the bag in the event of failure of the reducing valve; this, however, is unlikely if the apparatus is properly maintained.

(4) The carbon dioxide absorbent which fills the communicating compartment between the two halves of the breathing bag is so placed that air passing through the bag has to flow through the absorbent. The bag should not be violently shaken during use as this creates dust, but from time to time it should be gently kneaded with the hand or may be lightly shaken. This movement of the granules exposes fresh surfaces to absorb carbon dioxide from the exhaled breath; it also prevents *channelling*, which is the term used to describe the formation of passages through which the exhaled breath can flow freely without passing over sufficient granules for the carbon dioxide to be absorbed.

(5) To prevent misting during use, the eyepieces of the goggles, or the visor of a face mask, should be treated with anti-dim compound of the type recommended by the makers of the apparatus. This should be done after each time of use, and it will be found advantageous to treat the external surfaces as well as the internal ones to minimise fogging on the outer surfaces due to heat and smoke.

4 Minox breathing apparatus

The *Minox* is a closed-circuit oxygen set having a nominal duration of about 1 hour. The flow rate varies with the pressure of oxygen in the cylinder and initially may be up to 8 litres per minute, decreasing to zero when the cylinder is empty after about 90 minutes.

a. Description of the set

The set is carried on the back and is contained in a moulded glass fibre case with appropriate adjustable harness. The weight without breathing tubes or face mask is about 23·5 lb (10·7 kg). The breathing tubes lead from the lower left-hand side of the case under the arm to the wide vision face mask, or alternatively, if preferred, to a mouthpiece. The pressure gauge flexible tube leads from the lower right-hand side of the case under the arm and the gauge is secured to the right-hand shoulder strap. A low-cylinder-pressure warning whistle is connected between the gauge and the tube by means of an adaptor.

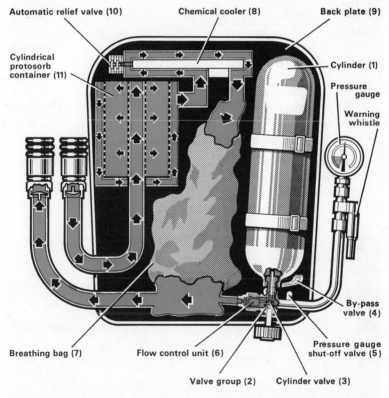

Fig. 4.8 Rear view of the *Minox* breathing apparatus with the cover removed showing the parts and a diagrammatic arrangement of the circuit of oxygen

A rear view of the set with the cover removed is shown in Fig. 4.8. The cylinder (1) has a capacity of 360 litres when charged to the normal pressure of 170 atmospheres. The valve group (2) is permanently attached to the cylinder and incorporates the cylinder valve (3), a lever-operated by-pass valve (4), pressure gauge shut-off valve (5) and a flow control unit (6). The breathing bag (7) is made of neoprene-coated terylene and has a capacity of about 5·5 litres. The metal canister type cooler (8) contains sodium phosphate in two separate compartments. The large capacity of the cooler allows the heated oxygen to pause for the maximum transference of heat; further cooling is obtained by radiation from the bag and conduction into the back plate (9). An automatic relief valve (10) which opens at a pressure of 1·5 ins (38 mm) water gauge is fitted to the cooling canister.

Protosorb is used as the carbon dioxide absorbent; this is not retained in the breathing bag, as with the *Proto* apparatus, but is held in the cylindrical metal container (11) in which is a removable perforated canister having an inner fine gauze tube, the absorbent being packed in the intervening space. This assembly when packed with about 2·5 lb (1·1 kg) of absorbent is screwed into the cylindrical container and sealed with a specially-formed rubber collar.

The principle of the breathing circuit is the same as that shown earlier in diagrammatic form in Fig. 4.1. Apart from the layout of the component parts of the apparatus, the two main differences between the *Minox* and the *Proto* are:

(1) there is no constant flow reducing valve;

(2) the set when in use is continually venting to atmosphere through the automatic relief valve.

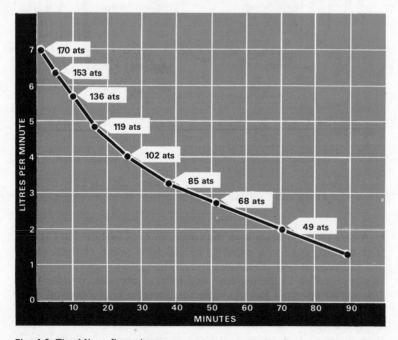

Fig. 4.9 The *Minox* flow chart

b. Flow control unit

The flow of oxygen from the cylinder to the bag is governed by the *flow control unit*. This has no moving parts, is sealed during manufacture and consists simply of a small-bore chromium capillary tube about 3 ft (900 mm) in length which is wound on a bobbin having a diameter of about ½-in (13 mm) and a length of about ¾-in (19 mm). The ends of this capillary tube terminate at the centre of the ends of the bobbin and are protected from dust particles and other foreign matter by sintered bronze filters.

When the cylinder valve is opened with a full cylinder charged to 170 atmospheres, the flow through the unit may initially be up to 8 litres per minute, but is usually about 7 litres per minute. This is, of course, considerably more oxygen than is needed by the wearer and the excess is discharged to atmosphere through the relief valve, thus allowing constant flushing of the breathing circuit while the set is in use. As the pressure in the cylinder drops, so does the flow, which reaches about 2 litres per minute after about 60 minutes. At this stage the cylinder contains a reserve of about 100 litres and the pressure is about 50 atmospheres. Flow will continue at a decreasing rate until the cylinder is exhausted, which state is reached after about 90 minutes. Fig. 4.9 shows a chart which gives the approximate flow in litres per minute at approximate pressures.

c. Working duration

It will be seen that the duration of the *Minox* breathing apparatus cannot be calculated in the same way as with the constant flow of 2·5 litres per minute of the *Proto* apparatus (*see* Part 2, Chapter 8, 'Working duration of breathing apparatus'). The full duration of the *Minox* when used by fire brigades and with a cylinder fully charged to 170 atmospheres, is taken to be when the rate of flow reaches 2 litres per minute. The working duration of *Minox* breathing apparatus is shown in Table 2 on page 95.

d. General

The initial starting-up procedure associated with closed-circuit apparatus is not necessary with the *Minox*. Starting up is as simple as that of compressed air. Maintenance also is simplified by the introduction of 'O' ring seals (Fig. 4.10), hand-tight connections and simple fittings for all component parts. The test procedure, however, is somewhat elaborate, and maintenance and testing should be carried out strictly in accordance with the instructions in the manufacturer's handbook using the appropriate equipment.

During servicing it is important that 'O' rings are examined periodically and renewed if necessary. It is also important that, if the by-pass valve has been dismantled, the disc springs on the by-pass spindle are re-assembled in the correct configuration as shown in the enlarged view in Fig. 4.10.

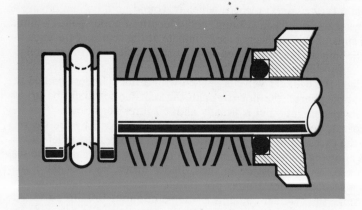

Fig. 4.10 Enlarged view of the *Minox* by-pass spindle showing the arrangement of the disc springs

5 Other oxygen breathing apparatus

Other types of oxygen breathing apparatus are available, but they are little used by fire brigades. These sets are, therefore, not described in detail, and the following notes are confined to the essential features.

a. Proto 2-hour breathing apparatus

The 2-hour version of the *Proto* apparatus is widely used by mines rescue teams in the United Kingdom. It is virtually the same as the 1-hour set, with the exception of the size of the cylinder and the quantity of the absorbent charge. Only a few brigades in the United Kingdom use this apparatus.

b. Salvus breathing apparatus

Apparatus of this type was at one time fairly extensively used by fire brigades, but it is now obsolete and the number of sets currently in use is negligible. The *Salvus*, which is a closed-circuit set similar in design and operation to the *Proto*, was intended for short-period use; it weighed about 18·5 lb (8·4 kg) and was carried on the chest. The cylinder capacity was 110 litres of oxygen when charged to a pressure of 132 atmospheres, and the constant flow reducer was designed to give a flow rate of 2 litres per minute. At a consumption at this rate, a full duration of 55 minutes would be achieved, but fire brigade work usually demands more than 2 litres per minute and the nominal duration of the set was reckoned to be about 30 to 40 minutes.

c. Lungovox breathing apparatus

This type of oxygen breathing apparatus is also of the closed-circuit type, but it has a constant flow of only 1·5 litres per minute, supplemented by a lung-governed demand valve which operates automatically to meet the needs of the wearer. The apparatus has a nominal duration of 2 hours and is carried on the back in a metal container.

6 Testing and maintenance

The following notes on care and maintenance apply to *Proto* apparatus and, except for the method of servicing the container for carbon dioxide absorbent, also to other types of oxygen apparatus referred to in this chapter.

Adjustments are seldom necessary to apparatus which is regularly serviced and tested, but the points detailed below should be carefully observed in connection with routine maintenance.

a. Testing

All oxygen breathing apparatus should be examined and tested at the times stipulated and in accordance with Test No. 3 in the *Fire Service Drill Book*.

b. After use

(1) Empty the bag, wash out with warm water, drain and dry thoroughly. Some brigades provide electric hot-air blowers for quick drying.

(2) Wash the breathing tubes, mouthpiece and goggles (or face mask) with yellow soap and warm water, using a suitable disinfectant. Get rid of moisture by shaking the tubes, and hang up to dry. Anti-dim as required.

(3) Generally clean the apparatus and harness.

c. During assembly

(1) Check the new cylinder contents with the standard test gauge; after removing the gauge apply a thin film of water to the outlet to ensure that the valve is not leaking in the closed position.

(2) If the cylinder pressure is less than five-sixths of its maximum charging pressure, replace it with a fresh one. (This also applies at all other tests and inspections.)

(3) Check the set gauge reading against that noted on the test gauge. If the reading of the standard gauge is slightly more than that of the gauge on the set the error can be ignored because there

will be more oxygen in the cylinder than indicated; but if the set gauge reads high and the error is 10 atmospheres or more, the gauge should be sent in for adjustment. This test should be made at various cylinder pressures.

(4) Ensure that all screwed connections have washers and that they are in good condition, that the relief valve is screwed tightly to its connection and that the diffuser is clear and in position.

(5) Check that the breathing bag is dry and undamaged, and charge with absorbent. This is supplied in airtight tins, each containing a complete charge, which should be poured into the breathing bag, care being taken to ensure that an equal amount goes into each side. As soon as the bag is charged, fasten the mouth by means of the metal clamp and wing nuts. Where the absorbent is carried in a metal canister, this is best filled by means of a hopper. If, however, the canister is filled by hand, the absorbent should be poured in until the container is full, then the sides of the canister should be lightly tapped to allow the absorbent to settle; the container should then be topped up with absorbent. The process should be repeated until no more absorbent can be added.

(6) When the apparatus is not in use the rubber plug should be fitted tightly into the mouthpiece to prevent air getting into the absorbent.

d. Cylinder valve

The cylinder valve is of robust construction and should call for no adjustment over long periods. Leaks and defects in the cylinder valve are normally discovered when testing the cylinder immediately prior to fitting it to the set (Test No. 3, Section 1(6) in the *Fire Service Drill Book*), or when the high-pressure test or the general check is carried out. Difficulty in turning on and off due to valve stiffness is a common fault and can usually be corrected by replacing the PTFE (polytetrafluoro-ethylene) washer.

Leaks in the open position may be due to a slack spindle nut giving insufficient tension on the spring; to a weak spring; to a slack gland nut; to a defective PTFE washer or to a damaged or bent spindle. The remedy in each case is to tighten or replace the defective part.

Leaks in the closed position are due to a scored or faulty seating on the screwed plug when the valve has been screwed down too tightly. The only remedy is to empty the cylinder, replace the screwed plug and have the cylinder recharged.

e. Reducing valve

The reducing valve of the *Proto* apparatus is set by the manufacturers to give a supply of 2·5 litres per minute; it should not be tampered with unless a flowmeter test shows that the rate of flow varies from this figure, and any adjustment should only be done by an experienced person.

The flow test (as detailed in Test No. 3, Section II, (1)(b) in the *Fire Service Drill Book*) is designed to check the performance of the reducing valve and it is during this test that any defects should be remedied. Slight adjustments to flow are easily made by using the adjusting collar which governs the degree of pressure exerted by the spiral spring upon the diaphragm. An alteration in the rate of flow can be effected by screwing in or out the adjusting collar according to whether the rate of flow is more or less than 2·5 litres a minute. Should, however, a major adjustment be necessary, a thorough check should be made to ascertain the cause before any adjustment is made. The defect which necessitates the alteration to the flow may be one of the following:

(1)   Defects which may result in a high flow

Fault	Remedy
By-pass valve defective; seating on valve plunger leaking.	Remove rocker arm assembly, complete with its carrier, withdraw the valve plunger and replace it with a new component.
Back-pressure disc slightly loose.	Tighten back-pressure disc locking screw.
Back-pressure disc washer defective.	Remove back-pressure disc locking screw and replace washer.
Floating valve seating set too far from inlet jet.	Remove blank cap, horseshoe washer and filling washer and adjust the floating valve to within a quarter to half a turn from inlet jet.
Floating valve seating severely scored or worn.	Remove blank cap, horseshoe washer and filling washer and replace floating valve with a new component.

(2)   Defects which may result in a low flow

Fault	Remedy
Filter screw choked with foreign matter.	Carefully remove filter screw, clean with an approved grease solvent and carefully replace.
Choked back-pressure disc.	Remove back-pressure disc locking screw and replace back-pressure disc.
Broken spring in adjusting sleeve.	Replace broken spring.
Floating valve set too close to inlet jet.	Remove blank cap, horseshoe washer and filling washer and adjust the floating valve to within a quarter to half a turn from inlet jet.
Choked inlet jet or central column.	Return to maker for repair.

(3)   Bobbin drops before the needle of pressure gauge reaches zero

Fault	Remedy
The pressure gauge has a plus error, or the gauge needle is sluggish or sticking when returning to zero.	Replace pressure gauge.
A slightly loose back-pressure disc or defective back-pressure disc washer.	Tighten down the back-pressure disc locking screw or replace washer.
A very slight leak from the by-pass valve, leaking into the system of the set.	Adjust the spring of the press-button using the adjusting screw, OR remove the rocker arm assembly, complete with its carrier, and replace the valve plunger.
Incorrectly adjusted floating valve.	Remove blank cap, filling washer and horseshoe washer and adjust floating valve to within a quarter to half a turn.
Damaged or worn seating on the floating valve.	As above, but replace floating valve.
A hard or perished diaphragm.	Completely strip the reducing valve and replace diaphragm.
Partial choke of the inlet jet or central column.	Completely strip the reducing valve and if possible clear the choke by using the jet cleaning adaptor. If this fails, return the valve group to the maker for repair.

When attempting to trace a reducing valve fault, the above sequence should be followed. It will be noted that the reducing valve is never stripped until all other possible faults have been eliminated. The occasions on which it is necessary to strip the reducing valve are rare. The valve is of robust construction and is designed to perform satisfactorily for years without attention.

After making the adjustment the horseshoe locking washer and the metal filling washer should always be inserted before the blank cap is screwed on. The cap should be screwed on tightly as any leak through the cap will affect the working of the reducing valve and will result in a loss of oxygen.

It is advisable before making any adjustments to the reducing valve as described above, to unscrew the valve group connecting nut and examine the gauze filter. This may be found to be dusty or coated with verdigris and may thus be impeding the flow of oxygen. It should be carefully removed with the tool provided for the purpose, cleaned with a suitable solvent and carefully replaced. If it is found to be punctured or damaged, it should be discarded and a new filter inserted.

f. Cooler

Calcium chloride and sodium phosphate will retain their properties almost indefinitely, but are subject to very slight loss, so they may need to be topped up at intervals to maintain the level in the cooler. To do this, a sufficient quantity of the coolant should be slowly heated until it liquefies, and then poured into the inner chamber after removing the screw cap at the end of the cooler. The cap should then be replaced and the cooler immersed in cold water to allow the contents to solidify.

g. Additional points to watch

(1) Where a lock bolt is fitted to the cylinder valve, it is better not to try to engage the bolt when the valve is closed. It is unlikely that the holes in the valve wheel will coincide with the bolt, and to attempt to make them do so may either damage the valve seating or leave the valve partially open.

(2) *No oil or grease of any kind should be used for lubricating the cylinder valve, gauge valve, reducing valve or other fittings.* Under no circumstances should oil or grease be allowed to come into contact with the breathing bag, mouthpiece or face mask. The action of oxygen on grease or oil causes rapid oxidation and may result in spontaneous combustion or an explosion.

(3) Undue force should never be used either on connecting nuts or on the cylinder valve. Force used on the cylinder valve may damage the thread and impair the seating of the valve. If difficulty is experienced in making any joint, a new washer should be fitted.

(4) The by-pass should never be opened whilst a flowmeter is connected, as this may damage the meter.

(5) Care should be taken not to knock or bang metal parts, such as the valve group, connecting nuts, etc., either when the set is being carried or when stowing it on the appliance, as such treatment may cause slight oxygen leaks which will be difficult to cure.

(6) Valves in breathing tubes should be examined periodically and renewed if they are defective or show signs of deterioration.

Chapter 5
Compressed-air breathing apparatus

After World War II interest in compressed-air breathing apparatus revived and the firm of Siebe Gorman, which hitherto had concentrated on the manufacture of oxygen sets, developed compressed-air sets. Other manufacturers also now produce compressed-air apparatus which is in use by fire brigades.

Compressed-air breathing apparatus is now more widely used by fire brigades than oxygen breathing apparatus. There are several reasons for this, namely, its wider general use by firemen, including retained firemen, the replacement of the now obsolete *Salvus* oxygen half-hour apparatus, and the introduction of ultra-lightweight cylinders which have a larger air capacity, thus increasing the duration of the set. A further but not inconsiderate factor is that compressed-air apparatus is more easy to service and maintain than oxygen apparatus.

1 General

Self-contained compressed-air breathing apparatus is designed on the open-circuit system. In this the exhaled air is discharged to the atmosphere and is not purified for re-use as in the oxygen closed-circuit system.

The main items of which compressed-air apparatus consists are: (*a*) a cylinder containing air under pressure, (*b*) a respiratory system which incorporates a means of reducing the pressure of the air from the cylinder and of supplying the wearer on demand with air according to his requirements, and (*c*) a face mask. The principles of operation are the same for all types of set; the difference between one make of set and another lies in the design of the reducing valves and the face mask.

In the majority of cases the apparatus has a single cylinder, and the standard one contains about 1200 litres of air (usually 1240 litres, but rounded off for convenience) when fully charged to a pressure of 132 atmospheres (1980 lbf/in).* Larger capacity cylinders are now available and are coming into more general use. These are of two types:

(a) a cylinder holding about 1800 litres when fully charged to 200 atmospheres (3000 lbf/in²);*

* See footnote on page 25.

(b) a special ultra-lightweight cylinder which contains 2250 litres when fully charged also to 200 atmospheres. In all cases the cylinder is carried on the wearer's back, attached to a suitable frame which forms part of the harness for securing the apparatus to the wearer's body.

The respiratory system may consist of a single-stage reducer or a two-stage reducer with the second stage incorporated in the face mask.

a. Duration of compressed-air apparatus

The duration of compressed-air apparatus varies considerably according to the amount of work done and the lung capacity of the wearer. From Table 1 it will be seen that when walking at a rate of 4 miles an hour (6·4 km/h), a man breathes about 37·3 litres of air per minute. At this rate of work a full cylinder (1240 litres) will have a duration of about 32 minutes. Fire brigade operations, however, often demand a higher rate of work and the consumption of air may be as high as 60 litres per minute, or even more for short periods, in which case the duration of the set would be correspondingly less. The average consumption is assumed to be 40 litres per minute and compressed-air breathing sets with a cylinder containing about 1200 litres of air are generally referred to as having a nominal duration of half an hour (but see Chapter 8 on the working duration of breathing apparatus).

Because compressed-air sets using the standard cylinder have a comparatively short duration, and since this duration can be affected appreciably by the wearer and the degree of work he is doing, it became customary to fit a low-cylinder-pressure warning device in the form of a whistle. However, since the 'Operational procedure for the use of breathing apparatus' (see Chapter 10) requires a 10-minute safety margin, the full duration of a set is reduced by this amount. As an additional safeguard to ensure that a wearer does not exceed the working duration of his set, low-cylinder-pressure warning whistles must now be fitted to all sets regardless of the capacity of the cylinder carried.

Due to their relatively short duration, compressed-air sets using a standard cylinder are generally used only when the risk is such that breathing apparatus is unlikely to be required for long periods, or as an inspection set particularly for officers. However, the increased duration available from the larger capacity cylinders has, as stated earlier in this chapter, contributed to the increase in the number of compressed-air sets in use and to the decline in the number of oxygen sets. The working duration of the 1800-litre cylinder when fully charged is 35 minutes, and that of the 2250-litre cylinder is 46 minutes.

b. Dressing

Dressing with the apparatus is relatively simple and the method is common to all types; when the arms have been placed through the shoulder straps, the body belt is tightened, all straps being adjustable. After opening the cylinder valve and checking the pressure gauge reading, the face mask is put on and the straps on the head-harness are adjusted.

After the apparatus is put on, a test is carried out to ensure that the face mask, exhaling valve, speech diaphragm and other fittings on the mask are leak-proof. The test may be carried out by squeezing or kinking the breathing tube (when this is possible) and inhaling; or by closing the cylinder valve and continuing to breathe until the air in the system is exhausted and it is impossible to inhale. The cylinder valve should, of course, be opened again immediately this stage is reached.

Masks generally in use have three pairs of straps on the head-harness. For correct positioning of the mask, the straps should be tightened in the following sequence: first, the two lower straps, then the middle pair and finally the upper pair, care being taken not to overtighten. Masks currently supplied with Siebe Gorman apparatus, however, have five straps, only four of which are adjustable. The fifth strap is permanently connected to the top of the mask. Should it be necessary to re-adjust the straps after carrying out the mask leak test, the same sequence should be adopted.

It will be seen that donning and starting up compressed-air breathing apparatus is much simpler than with oxygen apparatus. There is only one valve, the cylinder valve, to open, and there is no breathing bag to clear of nitrogen. Nevertheless, the precise method of donning and starting up any particular type of apparatus should be carried out carefully in accordance with the details in the maker's instruction book, as should any leak tests which they recommend.

c. Face masks

Face masks vary slightly as between one manufacturer and another, but all modern masks have full vision visors, are fitted with an exhaling valve (or breathing tubes in the case of those used with oxygen apparatus) and additionally are also fitted with a simple speech diaphragm. In some cases provision is also made for fitting a telephone microphone, if required.

The space which surrounds the face within the mask of a wearer is known as the *dead space*. Carbon dioxide from the exhaled breath tends to collect within that part of this space in which air circulates during breathing, and therefore the effective dead space is smaller than the actual space within the mask: how much smaller depends on the design of the mask.

An accumulation of carbon dioxide, however, in a mask has no ill effects on the wearer; it merely causes him to breathe more deeply. This has the effect of reducing the concentration of carbon dioxide, but the deep breathing has the effect of reducing the duration of the set.

In order to reduce the dead space to a minimum, provision is made in some masks for an *inner* mask, which fits over the nose and mouth so that the maximum duration may be obtained from the apparatus under all conditions.

It is virtually impossible to obtain a perfect gastight seal with face masks, despite considerable time and effort being spent over the years in order to improve the seal. Early masks were plain with no special sealing arrangement, the seal being made by the internal rubber surface of the mask. An improvement was made by fitting a reverted flap of relatively soft rubber inside the mask perimeter; further improvements on masks currently available are in the form of cushion seals. In one case the cushion filling is foam rubber and in another air. The air cushion, which should normally be kept at atmospheric pressure, adjusts itself to the contours of the face, being pushed in, for example, by high cheek bones. The air thus displaced causes a bulge in the cushion which forms into the lower contours of the face. Tests have also shown that the air cushion is one of the most effective seals so far produced.

Mask leakage may be outwards or inwards. Generally there are no special dangers with outward leakage except to reduce the duration of the apparatus. A hazard could arise under certain conditions when a mask is worn with an oxygen set, i.e. in exceptional cases where the leakage rate is high, in the form of a jet or stream, and glowing embers are present. Such a condition is unlikely to occur with air-cushion seal masks correctly fitted.

Inward leakage, however, does present problems. Recently published British Standards for breathing apparatus require the inward rate of leakage of a noxious gas to be not more than 500 parts per million of inhaled air. This is not acceptable for the concentrations of gases likely to be encountered, and the leakage rate for masks having air-cushion seals are generally considered lower than 500 parts per million where the men wearing the masks are clean-shaven. This may not be the case with men having beards or sideburns as these growths will generally prevent a satisfactory seal between mask and face.

Tests have indicated that the leakage rate into masks when worn by men having beards or sideburns varied just below 500 to over 5000 parts per million, and in a few cases where the growths were substantial the leakage rates were considerably higher. It is therefore important that breathing apparatus wearers should be clean-shaven in order that the best possible seal is obtained with the mask. An ill-fitting mask is not only of likely danger to the wearer, but also to the other member or members of the team who would need to render assistance should he be affected by inward leakage of his mask. In this connection, it should always be remembered that any breathing apparatus wearer who detects smoke or fumes in his mask, or has any reason to doubt the satisfactory operation of his set, should withdraw to fresh air immediately.

Inward leakage into face masks could be obviated if a positive pressure greater than ambient could be maintained within the mask. Progress is being made in this direction and sets of this type are currently being evaluated. This involves a modification to give an additional loading on the diaphragm of the demand valve which results in a higher pressure within the mask. The exhalation valve also has to be changed to open at a correspondingly higher pressure.

d. Types of compressed-air apparatus

There are three main manufacturers supplying compressed-air apparatus for fire brigade use in the United Kingdom:

(1) Siebe Gorman
(2) Normalair
(3) Roberts.

In recent years other manufacturers have entered the market, but at the time of going to press only a few of their apparatus have been purchased by one or two brigades for experimental purposes. The principal difference between the sets are in the face masks and the method of reducing the cylinder pressure and regulating the flow of air demanded by the wearer.

2 Siebe Gorman Mark IV compressed-air breathing apparatus

The Siebe Gorman Mark IV compressed-air breathing apparatus (Fig. 5.1) is a development of the three previous 'Marks' which were produced after World War II.

There are three main parts, comprising a full vision face mask, a respiratory system consisting of two stages for reducing the pressure of the air from the cylinder and automatically supplying the wearer with air as required, and the cylinder with a nylon carrying harness. The weight of the apparatus is approximately 30 lb (13·6 kg).

a. Description of the apparatus

The facepiece, or mask, is of moulded rubber with a wide vision perspex visor or window. It incorporates a lung-operated air demand valve which is the second stage of the two-stage reducer. The mask has an adjustable head-harness and includes a neckstrap or lanyard which lies around the neck for supporting the mask when it is not being worn on the face.

Fig. 5.1 Siebe Gorman Mark IV compressed-air breathing apparatus. (The distress signal warning unit has not been shown)

The apparatus consists of an alloy steel cylinder (Fig. 5.2(1)), a cylinder valve with protective rubber ring (2), a duralumin carrying frame (3) to which is attached adjustable shoulder straps and body belt, a main air supply tube (4), first-stage reducing valve (5), by-pass valve (6), air supply tube (7) from the first-stage reducing valve, the face mask (8), second-stage reducing valve (or demand valve) (9), pressure gauge tube (10), clip for pressure gauge (11), pressure gauge (12), pressure gauge shut-off valve (13) and the low-cylinder-pressure warning whistle (14).

The pressure of the air from the cylinder is reduced by means of the two-stage reducing valve, the first and second stages being shown in their relative positions on the apparatus in Fig. 5.2 (5) and (9) respectively. Both stages are shown in more detail in Figs. 5.3 and 5.4 respectively.

b. First-stage reducing valve

Air from the cylinder enters the first-stage reducing valve (Fig. 5.3) at (1) and passes through the fine gauze filter (2), along the drilled passages. From these it emerges at right angles through a $\frac{5}{64}$-in (2 mm) diameter jet (3). Opposite the jet is a fibre-seated valve (4)

51

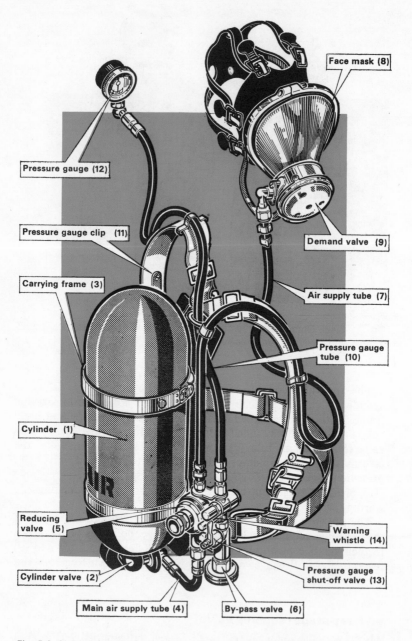

Pressure gauge (12)

Pressure gauge clip   (11)

Carrying frame (3)

Cylinder (1)

Reducing
valve (5)

Cylinder valve (2)

Main air supply tube (4)

By-pass valve (6)

Pressure gauge
shut-off valve (13)

Warning
whistle (14)

Pressure gauge
tube (10)

Air supply tube (7)

Demand valve (9)

Face mask (8)

Fig. 5.2 Siebe Gorman Mark IV compressed-air set, showing the various parts

which is screwed into the valve housing (5). The valve housing engages a projection on the inner diaphragm plate (6), which is screwed on to the outer diaphragm retaining plate (7). Between these two plates is a rubber diaphragm (8) which is held in position by the dome (9).

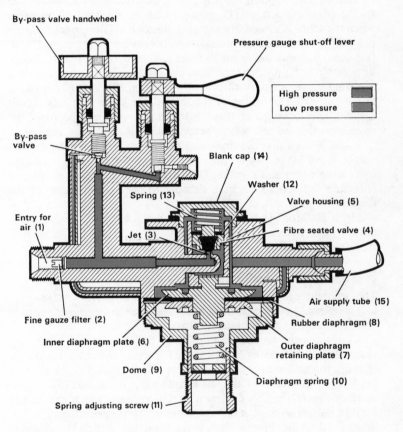

Fig. 5.3 Siebe Gorman Mark IV compressed-air set. The first-stage reducing valve

Any movement of the diaphragm (8) will result in a corresponding movement of the valve housing (5) and the valve (4). If the diaphragm is moved inwards, it will cause the valve to move away from the jet (3) allowing air to pass. Conversely, outward movement of the diaphragm will cause the valve to close the jet and shut off the air.

The diaphragm spring (10) is designed to force the diaphragm inwards, thus opening the valve. Air then enters the body of the reducing valve, and since it cannot escape (unless the wearer inhales) the pressure will build up. This pressure will act upon the flexible diaphragm (8) and force it outwards, causing the valve to shut off the air.

The pressure at which the air is shut off depends upon the force exerted by the diaphragm spring (10), and this is governed by the spring adjusting screw (11), which increases the shut-off pressure when the screw is turned inwards, i.e. clockwise. The correct pressure is 60 lbf/in² (4·1 bars). Formerly the pressure was set at 40 lbf/in² (2·8 bars) but was increased to meet the requirement that it should be possible to supply *two* men from one set. This is done by providing a second mask, a length of tubing, usually about 15 ft (4·6 m) long and a harness. The tubing of the second mask can be plugged into a quick-release coupling fitted into the air supply tube from the reducing valve on sets where second mask facilities are requested.

It will be seen that the first-stage reducing valve is similar to that on the *Proto* oxygen apparatus. The fibre-seated valve (4) is located by a washer (12) and a spring (13), held in position by a blank cap (14), and is fitted to act as a damper to prevent pulsation of the diaphragm.

Air at 60 lbf/in² (4·1 bars) pressure in the body of the first-stage reducer then passes through the air supply tube (15) to the second-stage reducing valve.

c. Second-stage reducing valve

The second-stage automatic lung-operated air delivery valve (Fig. 5.4) is referred to as the *demand valve*, because the air passed depends entirely on the demand made by the wearer.

Air reaches the second-stage jet (Fig. 5.4(1)), which is closed by the rubber-seated valve (2). The valve is pressed shut by the lever (3) through the action of the spring (4), which is adjustable by the nut (5). When the wearer inhales, air is drawn out of the box (6), i.e. the body of the valve. This creates a partial vacuum which causes the flexible rubber second-stage diaphragm (7) to deflect and move inwards. The diaphragm then presses on the lever (3), which is pivoted at (8); pressure is relieved from the valve (2) and air is passed to the wearer. The diaphragm is protected by a metal cover (9) held in position by three screws.

When the wearer inhales the non-return rubber inhalation valve (10) lifts, and the action of inhalation causes a partial vacuum in the box. On exhalation, the valve (10) closes and the partial vacuum is removed, the diaphragm returns to its original position and the spring (4) pulls on the lever (3) closing the valve (2), thus shutting off the air. The exhaled air passes through the non-return rubber valve (11) to atmosphere.

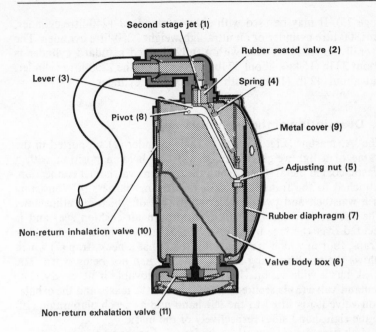

Second stage jet (1)

Rubber seated valve (2)

Lever (3)

Spring (4)

Pivot (8)

Metal cover (9)

Adjusting nut (5)

Rubber diaphragm (7)

Non-return inhalation valve (10)

Valve body box (6)

Non-return exhalation valve (11)

Fig. 5.4 Siebe Gorman Mark IV compressed-air set. The second stage or demand valve

d. Emergency by-pass valve

Should any fault develop in the first-stage reducer, an emergency by-pass valve (Fig. 5.3) is provided to ensure that the wearer receives a flow of air. The valve is operated by slightly opening the handwheel by turning it in an anti-clockwise direction.

e. Pressure gauge shut-off valve

In the event of damage to the pressure gauge or the pressure gauge tube, air may be shut off to these parts by operating the pressure gauge shut-off lever (Fig. 5.3) and closing the valve. Normally the valve should always be kept open.

3 Siebe Gorman 'Airmaster' compressed-air breathing apparatus

The 'Airmaster' is the successor to the Siebe Gorman Mark IV compressed-air set. As with the Mark IV, it is a two-stage self-contained set and has built-in facilities for air-line working (*see* page 75). It may be used with either a standard 1240-litre cylinder, an 1800-litre cylinder or an ultra-lightweight 2250-litre cylinder. The overall weight when used with a fully-charged standard cylinder is about 33 lb (15 kg), about 37 lb (16·8 kg) with the 2250-litre cylinder, but about 42 lb (19 kg) with the 1800-litre cylinder.

a. Description of the apparatus

The 'Airmaster' (Fig. 5.5) has a single cylinder (1) supported in the frame of a lightweight backplate (2) and held in position with a plastic-coated metal strap (3) and the reducing valve inlet connection. Attached to the frame is a terylene carrying harness (4) consisting of a waistbelt and two shoulder straps, all of which are adjustable. The rubber face mask (5) incorporates an air-cushion seal and is secured over the face by a suitable head-harness having five rubber straps, four of which are adjustable (6). It has a neck strap (7) which allows the mask to hang from the neck when not being worn. The mask has a wide vision visor which is removable if necessary. The demand valve (8) is secured to the front of the mask, and the exhalation valve (9) is fitted to the left-hand and a speech diaphragm (10) to the right-hand sides respectively of the mask.

High-pressure air from the cylinder is fed to the first-stage reducing valve (11) which is connected directly to the cylinder outlet. From the high-pressure side of the reducing valve a copper pipe (12) leads along the backplate to the pressure gauge tube (13) which lies over the left shoulder. An automatic shut-off valve (14) is fitted to the gauge and provides automatic isolation in the event of damage to the gauge. A low-cylinder-pressure warning whistle (15) is fitted to a 'T' junction in the copper pipe and can be seen through the cut-away portion of the cylinder in Fig. 5.5.

The main supply tube (16) for the mask is taken from the low-pressure side of the reducing valve and leads along the frame and over the right shoulder strap, where it terminates in a quick-release bayonet type connector (17). The mask supply hose (18) is fitted with a male connector (19) which mates with the female bayonet connector (17). This arrangement allows speedy replacement of the mask. The low-pressure side of the reducing valve is fitted with a bayonet type connector (20) to which may be connected a second mask, or when an air-line is used a 'Y' piece is provided so that the air-line can supply both the set and a second set. When the set is being used with an air-line, the cylinder valve should be closed. Both the bayonet type connectors close automatically by means of a spring-loaded valve when not in use, but the connector (17) has a small bleed hole so that, in the unlikely event of a leak from the reducing valve when the apparatus is left with the cylinder valve open and the demand valve supply hose is disconnected, the pressure build-up in the main supply tube is allowed to leak away.

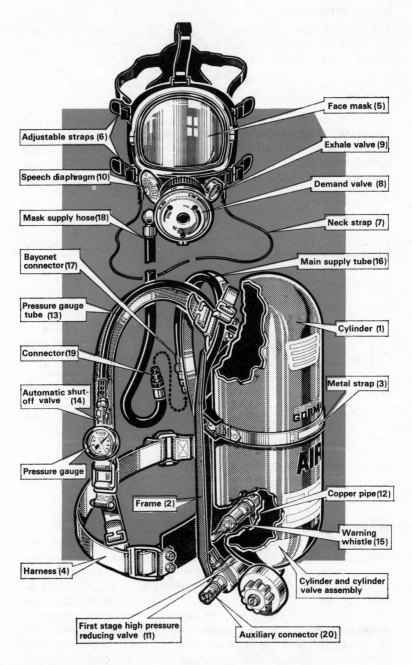

Face mask (5)

Adjustable straps (6)

Exhale valve (9)

Speech diaphragm (10)

Demand valve (8)

Mask supply hose (18)

Neck strap (7)

Bayonet connector (17)

Main supply tube (16)

Pressure gauge tube (13)

Cylinder (1)

Connector (19)

Automatic shut-off valve (14)

Metal strap (3)

Pressure gauge

Copper pipe (12)

Frame (2)

Harness (4)

Warning whistle (15)

Cylinder and cylinder valve assembly

First stage high pressure reducing valve (11)

Auxiliary connector (20)

Fig. 5.5 The 'Airmaster' compressed-air breathing apparatus

b. Demand valve

The demand valve is similar to that of the Mark IV apparatus, being of the diaphragm type upon which bears a spring-loaded lever operating a non-return inlet valve.

c. Reducing valve

The pressure-reducing valve (Fig. 5.6), unlike the diaphragm type of the Mark IV apparatus, is of the balanced piston type. In this a spring-loaded piston is balanced by the reduced pressure at which the reducer is set, which should be between 80 and 90 lbf/in² (5·5 and 6·2 bars) at a cylinder pressure of 132 atmospheres, and between

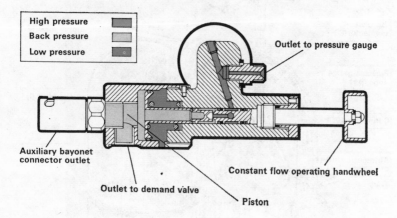

Fig. 5.6 The 'Airmaster' pressure-reducing valve

85 and 95 lbf/in² (5·9 and 6·6 bars) at a cylinder pressure of 200 atmospheres. The valve seating is an integral part of the piston, and when the pressure at the back of the piston is reduced by operation of the demand valve, the spring pushes the piston and its seating off the fixed jet, thus allowing air to pass through the piston to the low-pressure outlet. When the demand valve closes, the back pressure acting on the piston overcomes the spring pressure, and the piston moves forward to shut off the supply from the cylinder. Fig. 5.7 is an exploded view of the whole valve.

Provision is made for a constant flow of air to the mask if required. This is done by operating the constant flow by-pass valve by turning the red handwheel and reducing the spring pressure. This allows the reduced pressure to increase until it overcomes the resistance of the demand valve, thus providing a constant flow of air to the mask.

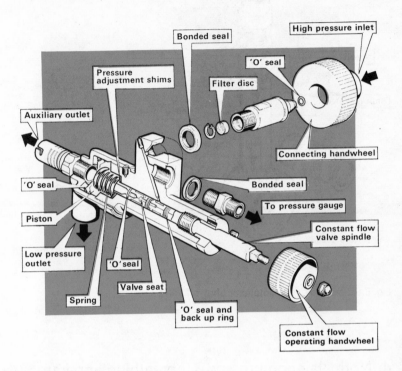

Fig. 5.7 Exploded view of the 'Airmaster' pressure-reducing valve

d. Low-cylinder-pressure warning whistle

Provision is made for slight adjustments of the operating pressure of the low-cylinder-pressure warning whistle (Fig. 5.5 (15)) should this become necessary. Whistles are set to give about 10 minutes' safety margin and the operating pressure should be between 40 and 45 atmospheres. Any adjustment should be carried out strictly in accordance with the maker's instructions.

e. Pressure gauge automatic shut-off valve

This valve (Fig. 5.8) cuts off the flow of air automatically should the gauge become damaged. It should be tested periodically by simulating a leak and a bleed screw is provided for this purpose. This test should be carried out in accordance with the manufacturer's instructions.

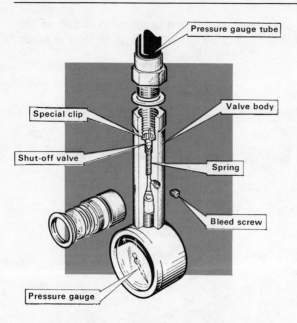

Fig. 5.8 Pressure gauge automatic shut-off valve

4 Normalair compressed-air breathing apparatus

Normalair apparatus was originally designed and manufactured by the makers of breathing apparatus used by the Himalayan Expedition in 1953. As with other makes of compressed-air breathing apparatus, it comprised basically a cylinder of air, a respiratory system for reducing the air pressure and a face mask. Several new features were claimed for the apparatus, not the least of which was the single-stage demand regulator which operated on a 'tilt' valve principle. The firm Normalair subsequently amalgamated with the German firm Draegerwerk AG, and is now known as Draeger Normalair Ltd. Since the introduction of the apparatus—the first set being model 880—it has, like that of other manufacturers, been developed, and two types are currently being produced:

(a) the A100, a single-stage set similar to the original but with several improvements;

(b) the A200, a two-stage version which has built-in facilities to allow the set to be used with an air-line as well as providing a 'second mask' attachment.

a. Draeger/Normalair A100 compressed-air breathing apparatus

(1) Description of the set

The set (Fig. 5.9) consists of a cylinder (1) mounted on a tough, light, thermo-plastics moulded backplate (2) supported on the back of the wearer by a synthetic fabric harness comprising adjustable padded shoulder straps and a waistbelt secured by a single buckle. The face mask (3) is secured by a head-harness (4) and incorporates a demand regulator (5), an expiratory valve/speech transmitter (6) and a perspex visor. The face mask is fitted with an inner mask (7) arranged to fit as closely as possible around the mouth and nose. The high-pressure air from the cylinder is supplied to the demand regulator and to the pressure gauge (8) by two flexible reinforced rubber hoses (9) having a working pressure of 3000 lbf/in² (207 bars). The hoses are connected to a 'Y' manifold at the top of the back plate; the longer hose passes over the right shoulder to the demand regulator and the other over the left shoulder to the pressure gauge. The gauge incorporates two built-in safety devices; the first is a relief valve which gets rid of any excess pressure in the case and removes the risk of the facepiece blowing out, and the second is a shut-off valve which allows air to pass for normal operation of the gauge, but shuts off immediately if there is a flow. This valve should be tested periodically in accordance with the maker's instructions by unscrewing the test screw provided.

The cylinder valve (10) is the only valve which has to be operated before using the set. A low-cylinder-pressure warning whistle (11) is fitted to the back plate and is connected to the high-pressure manifold by a 'T' union. The overall weight of the set when used with a fully-charged 1240-litre cylinder is about 29 lb (13 kg), about 32 lb (14·5 kg) with an ultra-light 2250-litre cylinder, but with an 1800-litre cylinder the weight is about 38 lb (17 kg).

(2) The face mask

The face mask (Fig. 5.9 (3)) is of moulded rubber, and in addition to the demand regulator (5), expiratory valve/speech transmitter (6) and the wide vision perspex visor, it incorporates breathing port adaptors made of moulded nylon; these are situated on each side and permit the mask to be used for other purposes if required. However, when the mask is used with compressed-air sets, the demand regulator (5) is screwed into the left-hand adaptor and the other is fitted with a blanking plug (12). Fabric reinforced rubber bosses on the outside of the mask rim carry six metal quick-release buckles which secure the head-harness. The harness is a rubber moulding with six straps which are ribbed to prevent slipping.

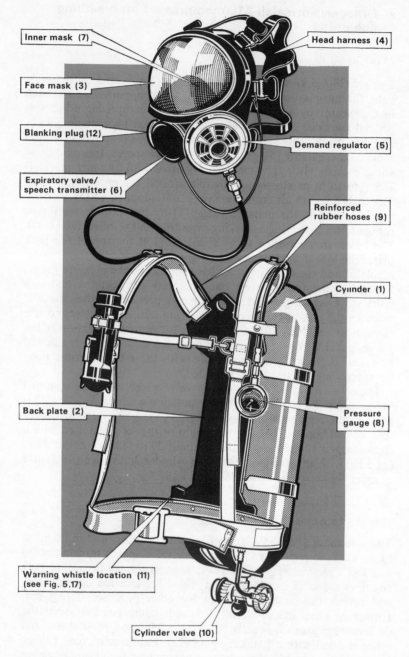

Inner mask (7)

Head harness (4)

Face mask (3)

Blanking plug (12)

Demand regulator (5)

Expiratory valve/
speech transmitter (6)

Reinforced
rubber hoses (9)

Cylinder (1)

Back plate (2)

Pressure
gauge (8)

Warning whistle location (11)
(see Fig. 5.17)

Cylinder valve (10)

Fig. 5.9 Draeger/Normalair A100 compressed-air breathing apparatus

A bonded air-cushion seal round the inside edge of the mask (Fig. 5.10 (1)) contains air at atmospheric pressure and forms a leak-proof seal on the face with only light tension on the adjusting straps. The air is sealed into the cushion by a bronze ball (2) and the cushion

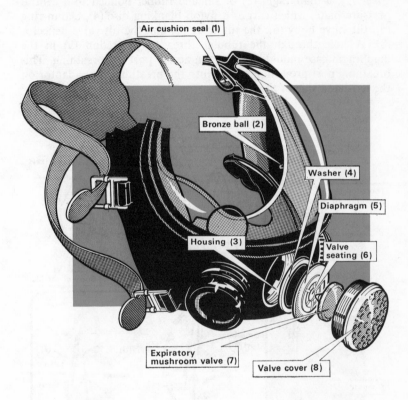

Fig. 5.10 Draeger/Normalair face mask showing air-cushion seal and the expiratory valve/speech transmitter

adjusts itself to the contours of the face when the mask is put on. Air-deflecting flanges assist in demisting by directing inspired air over the perspex visor. Projections on the inner rims of the breathing port adaptors prevent any risk of the deflecting flanges interfering with the free passage of air.

Also shown in Fig. 5.10 is an exploded view of the expiratory valve/speech transmitter. This comprises a housing (3), washer (4), moulded nylon diaphragm (5) with the expiratory valve seating (6) in the centre and an expiratory rubber mushroom valve (7), which is located in a central hole in the valve seat. The diaphragm is sealed in the valve housing by the screwed valve cover (8).

(3) The demand regulator

The demand regulator is a single-stage reducer consisting basically of a tilt valve and a diaphragm housed in a suitable casing. The regulator consists of the regulator body (Fig. 5.11 (1)), the body cover (2), a diaphragm (3) of silicone rubber bonded to a central pressure plate, which carries a nylon blanking disc (4), clamp ring (5), tilt valve body (6), the tilt valve (7) and the tilt valve deflector (8). A hole through the tubular threaded projection (9) in the diaphragm case moulding forms an access port for breathing. This breathing port projection screws into the breathing port adaptor on the left-hand side of the mask.

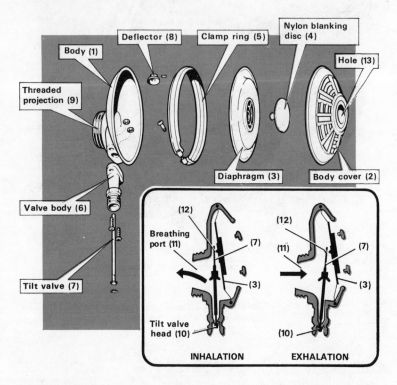

Fig. 5.11 Draeger/Normalair demand regulator. Inset: diagrammatic arrangement of the operation of the tilt valve

The regulator is simple in design and the arrangement of the tilt valve operation is shown in Fig. 5.11 (inset). The tilt valve spindle (7) projects through the housing and the deflector into the lower half of the diaphragm case, and the head of the tilt valve (10) is held in the closed position on its seating in the valve housing by the pressure of air from the cylinder. Inhalation through the breathing port (11) creates a partial vacuum within the face mask which causes the diaphragm (3) to move inwards and press against the spindle at (12), so tilting the valve from its seating at (10) and permitting a flow of air from the cylinder. Exhalation causes the diaphragm (3) to move outwards away from the valve spindle (7), allowing the tilt valve to reseat and cut off the supply of air at (10).

The performance of the regulator is such that the wearer is supplied with whatever air he requires. During light work and shallow breathing, the valve tilts slightly, allowing only a small volume of air to pass. Harder work and deeper breathing causes greater tilting of the valve and consequently the flow of air is increased. At normal rates of work, the suction effort is only about $\frac{1}{2}$-in (13 mm) of water gauge, and at the top peak of exertion is no more than 1 in (25 mm). This performance is inherent in the design and no adjustment is required.

As the demand regulator provides ample air for the highest possible rate of work, no by-pass is required. The regulator is so designed, however, that it may be manually operated, if required, by pressing on the diaphragm through the 1-in (25 mm) diameter hole in the centre of the outer casing (Fig. 5.11 (13)). This action causes the diaphragm to press against the tilt valve spindle, lifting the valve from its seating as during inhalation, and allowing air into the system.

(4)   Cylinder and manifold assembly

The cylinder, the neck of which is cradled by the curved bottom (Fig. 5.12 (1)) of the backplate, is secured in position by two stainless-steel straps (2) tightened by thumbscrews (3). The manifold assembly (4) is positioned on the backplate; it consists of a nickel-plated copper pipe (5) to which is connected a short length of high-pressure flexible hose (6) terminating in a finger-tight cylinder valve connection at the lower end. At the upper end is a 'Y' manifold (7) to which the high-pressure hoses for the demand regulator and the pressure gauge are connected. Near the bottom of the pipe is a 'T' junction (8) to which the low-cylinder-pressure warning whistle (9) is fitted.

The set can be supplied for use with four types of cylinder: 1240 litres at 132 atmospheres, 1800 litres at 200 atmospheres and 2250 litres at 200 atmospheres, all of which are about 7 ins (180 mm) in diameter and are interchangeable when used with the standard strap. The fourth type of cylinder, however, i.e. 1200 litres at 200 atmospheres, is only $5\frac{1}{2}$ ins (140 mm) in diameter and smaller straps are required to secure it.

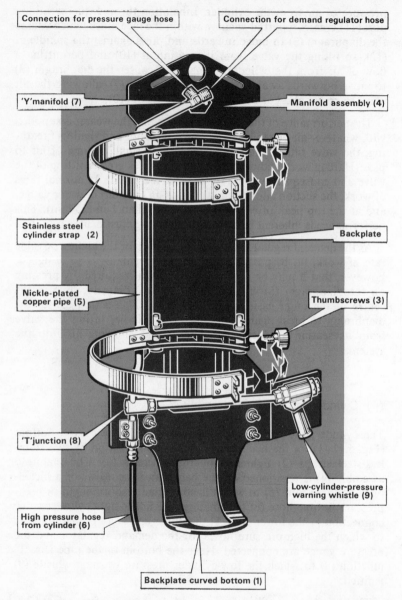

Connection for pressure gauge hose

Connection for demand regulator hose

'Y'manifold (7)

Manifold assembly (4)

Stainless steel
cylinder strap (2)

Backplate

Nickle-plated
copper pipe (5)

Thumbscrews (3)

'T'junction (8)

Low-cylinder-pressure
warning whistle (9)

High pressure hose
from cylinder (6)

Backplate curved bottom (1)

Fig. 5.12 Rear view of the Draeger/Normalair A100 backplate showing the manifold assembly

b. Draeger/Normalair A200 compressed-air breathing apparatus

The A200 is a development of the A100 apparatus, but modified so that it can be used in conjunction with air-line equipment. From Fig. 5.13 it will be seen that basically the set is similar to the A100, so it is proposed here only to refer briefly to those items which are different.

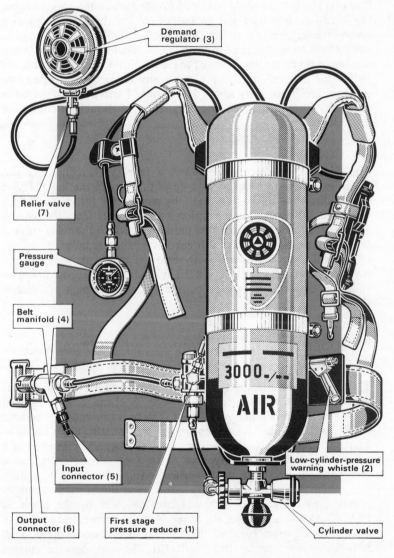

Fig. 5.13 Draeger/Normalair A200 breathing apparatus without face mask

(1) General

The A200 has two stages. High-pressure air from the cylinder is fed into the first-stage balanced piston type pressure reducer (Fig. 5.13 (1)). The reducer feeds high-pressure air to a manifold which supplies the low-cylinder-pressure warning whistle (2) and the hose of the pressure gauge. Low-pressure air from the pressure reducer, at a regulated pressure of 110 lbf/in^2 (7·6 bars) (plus or minus 10 lbf/in^2 (0·7 bars), is fed to the demand regulator (3) and to the belt manifold (4). The belt manifold has two low-pressure connectors, an input (5) for an air-line feed and an output (6) for the attachment of a second mask. These connectors are closed automatically when not in use and are opened automatically when connections are made. When working with an air-line attached to the manifold, air is automatically fed to the demand regulator without any restrictive valve, air-line pressure being normally about 100 lbf/in^2 (7 bars). When the set is being fed from an air-line, the cylinder valve should, of course, be kept closed.

(2) Demand regulator

The demand regulator incorporates a relief valve (Fig. 5.13 (7)) which is designed to lead a build-up of pressure in the low-pressure system directly into the face mask, by-passing the tilt valve. The tilt valve will not operate on inhalation if the pressure from the reducer exceeds 160 lbf/in^2 (11 bars), the pressure at which the relief valve is set. In the unlikely event of a breakdown of the reducer, the excess of air will therefore flow directly into the mask. In such circumstances, the wearer should adjust the cylinder valve in order to obtain sufficient air without wastage or discomfort from high pressure in the mask.

5 Roberts Mark 101 compressed-air breathing apparatus

The first Roberts breathing apparatus was the Mark 41. This set, as stated earlier, was produced by Roberts, McLean & Co Ltd, and was based on the French *Mandet* set. The firm subsequently became SF Roberts Ltd, and is now known as SF Roberts (1960) Ltd. The Mark 41 apparatus weighed about 44 lb (20 kg) and consisted of a general service respirator type of mask, twin air cylinders and a lung-controlled respiratory system housed in a breathing bag. Subsequent developments led to the production of the Mark 54, a single-cylinder, two-stage set which was later followed by the Mark 54 PFV. This set was basically the Mark 54 with an improved face mask and breathing tube. None of these sets is now manufactured as all have been replaced by the Mark 101, the one now in current production.

a. Description of the apparatus

The Mark 101 is a two-stage open-circuit set which may be used

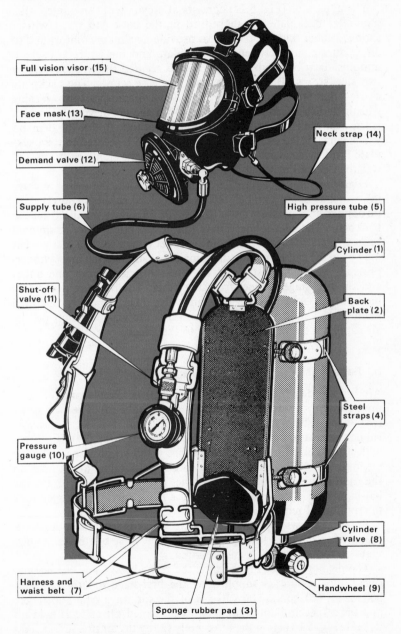

Full vision visor (15)

Face mask (13)

Demand valve (12)

Neck strap (14)

Supply tube (6)

High pressure tube (5)

Cylinder (1)

Shut-off valve (11)

Back plate (2)

Steel straps (4)

Pressure gauge (10)

Cylinder valve (8)

Harness and waist belt (7)

Handwheel (9)

Sponge rubber pad (3)

Fig. 5.14 The Roberts Mark 101 compressed-air breathing apparatus

with the standard 1240-litre cylinder, or alternatively with the 1800- or 2250-litre cylinders. If the set is likely to be required for use with air-line equipment, it can be supplied with the necessary adaptations.

The apparatus (Fig. 5.14) consists of a cylinder (1) mounted on a mild-steel backplate (2) shaped to fit the back and fitted with a sponge-rubber 'kidney' pad (3) to provide maximum comfort and to allow an air gap between the backplate and the wearer's back to minimise heat build up. The cylinder is secured to the backplate by two steel straps (4) fastened by quick-release screws. The backplate carries the first-stage reducer, the low-cylinder-pressure warning whistle and the high-pressure tube (5) for the pressure gauge, which is led over the left shoulder, and the supply tube (6) for the demand valve, which is led over the right shoulder. Also secured to the backplate is a terylene harness, which consists of the shoulder straps and waistbelt (7), all of which are adjustable.

High-pressure air from the cylinder is fed via the cylinder valve (8), which is opened and closed by a moulded rubber handwheel (9) through a high-pressure hose to a small three-way manifold on the backplate. The inlet connection of this hose is fitted with two sintered bronze filters to prevent entry into the set of any foreign matter that may be in the cylinder. This small manifold supplies the low-cylinder-pressure warning whistle and the pressure gauge from one outlet and the first-stage reducer from the other. The pressure gauge (10) incorporates a slide-type shut-off valve (11) which is operated manually by sliding the member towards the gauge to shut off the air supply in the event of damage to the gauge.

b. Face mask and demand valve

Air for the demand valve (Fig. 5.14 (12)) is taken from the low-pressure side of the reducer via the supply tube (6). The face mask (13) is of soft moulded natural rubber and has six adjustable rubber head straps and a nylon lanyard or neck strap (14). It is fitted with a foam-filled cushion seal and has a full vision visor (15). The demand valve (12) incorporates a speech diaphragm, and a boss on the right-hand side of the mask carries the exhalation valve. On the left-hand side of the mask provision is made for fitting a telephone microphone if required.

Fig. 5.15 shows the exhalation valve which is secured in the mask by an adaptor fitted through the port. The valve can be easily dismantled for examination and cleaning.

The demand valve (Fig. 5.16) is the second stage and the normal operating pressure as supplied by the first-stage reducer is about 300 lbf/in^2 (20 bars). The valve is of the tilt valve type and incorporates a speech diaphragm. The nylon-seated tilt valve is held on its seat (Fig. 5.16 (1)) in the brass body (2) by the air pressure behind it and is centralised by the conical spring (3) fastened to the valve

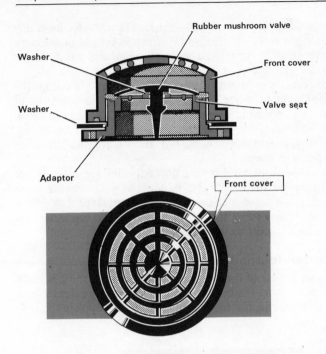

Rubber mushroom valve

Washer

Washer

Adaptor

Front cover

Valve seat

Front cover

Fig. 5.15 Roberts Mark 101 exhalation valve assembly

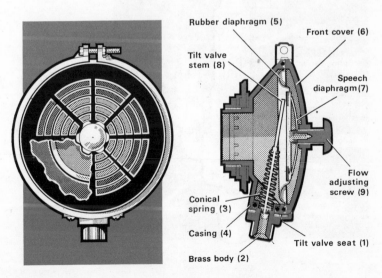

Rubber diaphragm (5)

Front cover (6)

Tilt valve
stem (8)

Speech
diaphragm (7)

Flow
adjusting
screw (9)

Conical
spring (3)

Casing (4)

Brass body (2)

Tilt valve seat (1)

Fig. 5.16 Roberts Mark 101 second-stage demand valve

stem. The plastic-moulded casing (4) houses the tilt valve assembly and the moulded rubber diaphragm (5) which is held in position by the front cover (6). The demand valve diaphragm carries at its centre a stretched silk speech diaphragm (7).

Inhalation creates a slight vacuum in the mask, causing the demand diaphragm to move inwards and contact the stem (8) of the tilt valve. The resulting deflection of the stem unseats the valve, admitting a volume of air proportional to the depth of breathing. On exhalation the diaphragm is pushed away from the tilt valve stem, allowing it to reseat.

Mounted on the front cover (6) is a flow adjusting screw (9). When screwed in it causes the diaphragm to push against the tilt valve stem, unseating the valve and so providing a constant flow of air infinitely variable according to the adjustment of the screw and the amount by which the tilt valve is unseated.

c. Whistle manifold and first-stage reducer

Fig. 5.17 shows a view of the low-cylinder-pressure warning whistle. High-pressure air from the cylinder flows through the cylinder hose (1) to the connector in the manifold (2) where it supplies the low-

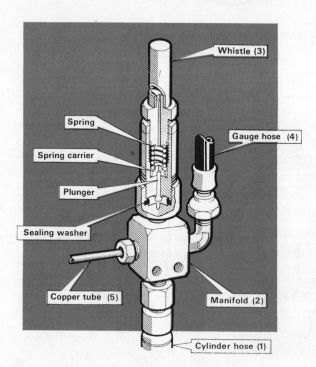

Fig. 5.17 Low-cylinder-pressure warning whistle

cylinder-pressure warning whistle (3) and the pressure gauge through the hose (4). Air is also supplied to the first-stage reducing valve via the copper tube (5).

The first-stage reducing valve (Fig. 5.18) is designed to give a constant output (intermediate) pressure with a cylinder pressure varying from 3000 to 300 lbf/in² (207 to 20·7 bars). The valve is of the balanced piston type and consists of the body (1) having an inlet (2) and an outlet (3) which supplies the demand valve. Inside the body is a nylon piston (4), sealed at each end with an 'O' ring and having a conical valve seat. The piston valve is held off its seating initially by the spring (5) and when the cylinder valve is opened, air is admitted past the valve seating into the piston via the transverse

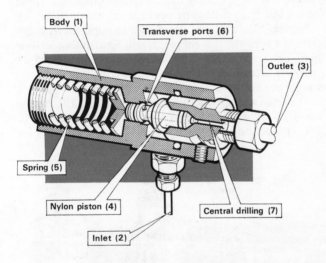

Body (1)

Transverse ports (6)

Outlet (3)

Spring (5)

Nylon piston (4)

Central drilling (7)

Inlet (2)

Fig. 5.18 Detail of the first-stage reducing valve

ports (6) and discharged through the central drilling (7) to the outlet. Flow continues until the pressure at the outlet, which also acts on top of the piston, reaches about 300 lbf/in² (20·7 bars), at which pressure it overcomes the force of the spring and closes the valve. On inhalation the demand valve opens and the pressure in the supply hose is reduced, whereupon the spring pushes the piston valve off its seating allowing the reducer valve to re-open. This action continues until the cylinder pressure falls to 300 lbf/in² (20·7 bars), after which the valve remains open until the cylinder is empty.

As the nylon piston is the only moving part, the possibility of failure is remote. However, should the valve stick in the open position, the full cylinder pressure will then appear at the demand valve on the mask. This will result only in a stiffening of the mask supply hose and a slight increase in breathing resistance, but the apparatus will continue to operate properly. Should the valve stick in the closed position the air supply to the mask will be cut off, but this can be restored by operating the by-pass handwheel.

After the pressure is reduced, the air passes through the outlet on the low-pressure side of the reducer to the supply hose and on to the demand valve. Facilities are also provided for an air-line to be connected or for a second mask to be attached.

6 Air-line equipment

The use of air-line equipment has been recommended for fire-fighting purposes subject to it being used only under certain conditions. These conditions are set out in Part 2: 'The operational use of breathing apparatus', Chapter 13, 'The use of air-line equipment for fire fighting', and from a study of this chapter it will be seen that air-line equipment may be worn either with or without compressed-air breathing apparatus according to circumstances.

Men, who must always work in pairs, are supplied with air by a single line of hose from a supply point equipment (Fig. 5.19), having initially a supply of about 4500 litres of compressed air in two or more cylinders (1) according to capacity. High-pressure air from the

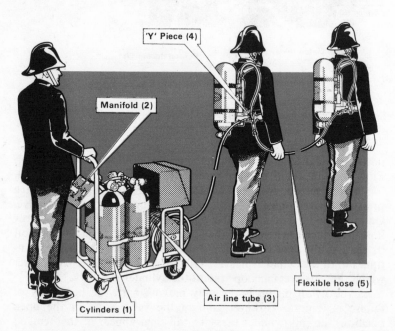

Fig. 5.19 Men being supplied with air by means of air-line equipment

cylinders is reduced to a line working pressure of about 100 lbf/in² (7 bars) by means of a pre-set reducer valve incorporated in a manifold (2) to which all cylinders are connected. Facilities are provided to enable a rapid switch from empty to fully-charged cylinders as required. The air-line hose (3) terminates in a 'Y' piece (4) attached to the belt or harness of the breathing set of the second man of the pair. One branch of the 'Y' is connected to the mask of the second man and the other to the leading man by means of a flexible hose (5) not more than 10 ft (3 m) in length. When breathing apparatus is worn with air-line equipment, the air from the cylinder on the set is held in reserve for emergency purposes, the cylinder valve being kept closed until required.

It is considered that the maximum length of the air-line should not exceed 300 ft (91 m), although normally it will probably not be possible to penetrate more than about 200 ft (61 m) because of the drag of the hose and the resistance caused by feeding round corners, etc., *en route*. It should be remembered that, whereas in an emergency men wearing breathing apparatus can disconnect the air-line and withdraw using the cylinder on their sets, men not wearing breathing apparatus will be impeded in their withdrawal by having to make up the air-line on their way out.

7 Testing and maintenance

a. Testing

All compressed-air breathing apparatus should be examined and tested at the times stipulated and in accordance with Test No. 3 (Sections I and III) in the *Fire Service Drill Book*.

b. Maintenance

The care and maintenance of all compressed-air breathing apparatus is relatively simple. Adjustments are seldom necessary, especially if the sets are regularly used and serviced. Dismantling, assembling, testing and the renewal of any of the component parts should be carried out in accordance with the manufacturers' recommendations for each type of set. The following points, however, should be observed during routine maintenance of all sets:

(1) After use the apparatus should be cleaned as necessary.

(2) The face mask should be washed and disinfected. The whole apparatus should be thoroughly dried before reassembly. Valves and other parts should be examined and renewed as necessary in accordance with the makers' instructions.

(3) The visor should be anti-dimmed.

(4) If the cylinder pressure is less than five-sixths of the maximum

charging pressure, the cylinder should be replaced by a fully-charged one.

(5) Washers or other parts found defective during tests should be renewed. 'O' rings and other seals should be renewed not less frequently than recommended by the makers.

(6) When tightening nuts, excessive force should be avoided as this may damage the threads. It should be noted that certain connections, e.g. cylinder connectors, are tightened only by hand and cannot be removed when the cylinder valve is open and the set is pressurised. To remove such connectors, the cylinder valve should be closed and the demand valve diaphragm actuated so as to release the pressure in the set.

(7) Oils or grease should not be allowed to come into contact with any part of the apparatus. Where manufacturers recommend the use of a silicone compound to act as a lubricant on certain parts, this should be used sparingly and no substance other than that recommended and available from the manufacturers should be used.

(8) Due to the comparatively thin walls of the ultra-lightweight cylinders, they are more susceptible to damage than the conventional type of cylinder. The manufacturers issue special instructions on the care and maintenance of the ultra-lightweight cylinder and these should be carefully followed, using only the materials recommended.

Chapter 6
Other breathing apparatus equipment

1 Low-cylinder-pressure warning whistles

Low-cylinder-pressure warning whistles are a requirement of the 'Operational Procedure for the use of breathing apparatus', and whistles are fitted as standard on both oxygen and compressed-air sets. The provision of the whistle in no way relieves a breathing apparatus wearer of his responsibility to refer to his gauge from time to time to assess the contents of his cylinder, particularly as hard work may reduce the working duration time of the set as this is based on average consumption. The whistle should be regarded solely as an additional safeguard to ensure that men will not continue working beyond the safe working duration of their sets.

Whistles (*see* Fig. 5.17 on page 72) are set to operate so as to provide a breathing apparatus wearer with a safety margin of about 10 minutes to allow him to return to fresh air and his entry control. In the case of *Proto* sets, the whistles should be set to operate when the cylinder is at one-quarter of its maximum pressure so that theoretically the set has 15 minutes to run. In fact, however, whistles consume up to 2 litres per minute, and so the actual safety margin with these sets is therefore about 10 minutes. In order to conserve oxygen in case of emergency and when the 'entrapped procedure' (*see* page 103) is put into operation, means must be provided to permit the whistle to be shut off on all oxygen sets. With compressed-air sets, the whistle consumption is ignored as 2 litres per minute is small in relation to the amount of air breathed.

2 Distress signal warning units

A further safeguard to breathing apparatus wearers is the provision with each set of a device which can be manually operated by the wearer to give an audible warning should he become distressed for any reason. These devices are known as *distress signal warning units* (DSUs) and are so designed that once they are operated they cannot be switched off without the use of a special key. The key is kept permanently attached to the set tally, and as the tally is handed by the wearer to the Breathing Apparatus Control Officer before entering an incident, it follows that having switched on the alarm signal the wearer must return to the control before the DSU can be switched off.

A specification (JCDD/19/1) for the warning unit has been pre-pared by the Joint Committee on Design and Development of Appliances and Equipment. The units, which are about the size of a hand torch, comprise basically a casing into which is fitted a horn or buzzer unit, a switch and a battery; the weight of the unit must not be more than 22 oz (624 g). It is recommended that regardless of the type of set worn, the unit should be carried in a standard position on the right-hand side at chest height with the horn facing down-wards (Fig. 6.1).

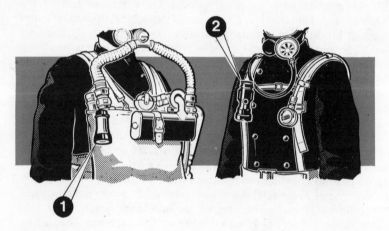

Fig. 6.1 The position in which the distress signal warning unit is to be carried. (1) On an oxygen set; (2) on a compressed-air set

The specification requires the units to be battery-operated and to be intrinsically safe. Early units were powered by the standard SP2 type of battery, but following an amendment to the specification to permit the use of high-powered batteries, e.g. HP2, Mallory, MN1300, or equivalent, a further intrinsic safety certificate was necessary for units in which this type of battery could be used. High-power types of battery must not be used with the early units unless these have been modified, and in all cases they should only be used with units on which the intrinsic safety certificate number is prefixed 'EX'.

So far as the sound intensity of the units is concerned, the speci-fication requires this to be 90 decibels at 6 ft (1·8 m) at a frequency of between 3250 and 3750 cycles per second (3·25 to 3·75 kHz). A further requirement is that the units must be able to withstand tem-porary submergence in water without being put out of action.

Two makes of DSU complying with specification JCDD/19/1 are currently available: the *Draeger/Normalair* and the *Diktron*.

a. Draeger/Normalair distress signal unit

The Normalair DSU (Fig. 6.2) has a shock-proof rubber casing (1), is about 7 in (178 mm) long and weighs about 20 oz (567 g). A strap (2) is provided for attaching the unit to a breathing apparatus. The

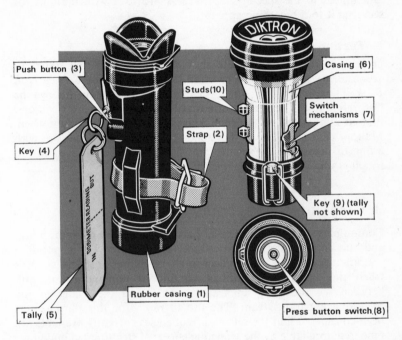

Fig. 6.2 Distress signal warning units. Left: the Draeger/Normalair. Right: the Diktron.

unit is operated by depressing the pushbutton (3) which operates a micro-switch; it cannot then be switched off without the use of the special key (4) which is normally affixed to the tally (5) of the breathing apparatus set. To stop the horn, the key is inserted and turned through 90 degrees. Maintenance, including dismantling and assembly, should be carried out in accordance with the maker's instructions.

b. Diktron distress signal unit

Fig. 6.2 shows the Diktron DS3 unit which is in current production. The body or casing (6) is of heavy gauge aluminium alloy with rubber shock absorbers at each end. The sealed switch mechanisms (7) are silver-plated for reliable long-term operation. The unit is operated by depressing the press-button switch (8) situated in the base of the unit. The button can only be released by the special key (9) which, after being inserted into the centre of the button, is turned in an anticlockwise direction and then clockwise, the two unlocking positions being clearly felt.

Two studs (10) are fitted to the casing to allow quick release and attachment to the special snap harness provided with the unit for securing it to a breathing apparatus.

c. Testing of distress signal warning units

Distress signal warning units should be examined and tested in accordance with Test No. 3, (Section IV (2)), in the *Fire Service Drill Book*. The examination, which is carried out at the same time as the test, refers to the need to ensure that battery contacts are clean and that no sulphation has occurred. This is particularly important where Mallory cells are used, as they tend to 'frost' over at the base with a film of potassium carbonate. This film should be removed with a rough cloth.

3 Communications equipment

Communications are an essential part of breathing apparatus work, and the communications procedure (*see* Chapter 11) is put into operation as directed by the officer-in-charge at fires or special services when the situation requires a continuous communication link between the breathing apparatus control and the leader of the breathing apparatus team. The use of radio for this purpose has been considered, but the sets and frequencies currently available are rendered unreliable by the screening effects of steel-framed buildings. The present method of maintaining continuous communications link is therefore by a telephone line, although experimental work to find a suitable radio system is continuing.

a. Specifications

A requirement specification for communications equipment for use with breathing apparatus (JCDD/19/2) has been prepared by the Joint Committee on Design and Development of Appliances and Equipment. The specification provides for two types of equipment, one using a microphone and earpiece, and the other a microphone and a transistorised amplifier with a loudspeaker unit. At least 300 ft (91 m) of cable, carried in a suitable container and having plugs and sockets at each end for connecting to the apparatus or for extending the cable, must be provided with either type. The cable must be suitably marked to indicate the direction from which it was laid so that it can be used as a guide-line if necessary.

The cable and equipment worn by the leader of a breathing apparatus team must carry a certificate of intrinsic safety and must not be put out of action by being submerged in water. There are two types of equipment complying with the specification currently available; these are the Draeger/Normalair 'Southampton' equipment, developed in collaboration with the Southampton Fire Brigade, and the Diktron equipment manufactured by Diktron Developments Ltd.

b. 'Southampton' communications equipment

The method of communication used by the 'Southampton' equipment is microphone and earpieces. The team leader is equipped with a standard face mask fitted with a microphone and a single earpiece. Connection between the team leader and the Breathing Apparatus Control Officer is by a cable carried in a canvas container secured to the wearer's harness. The cable, marked throughout its length with arrows pointing in the direction from which it was laid, pays out as the wearer moves away from the control point (Fig. 6.3). Care should be taken when stowing the cable in its container that the arrows are pointing in the right direction to ensure that they indicate the way out.

Fig. 6.3 The 'Southampton' communications equipment showing the method of connection between the team leader and the controller at the control point

The controller at the B A Control point is equipped with a twin earpiece-telephone headset and a boom microphone. These are connected to a control box carried in a frontal position by means of a neck sling. The control box houses the battery. Provision is made on the control box for connection with two team leaders via separate cables, or one team leader and an additional officer at the control, who is also equipped with a headset. This facility allows, for example, a senior officer to talk directly with a team leader instead of through the control officer.

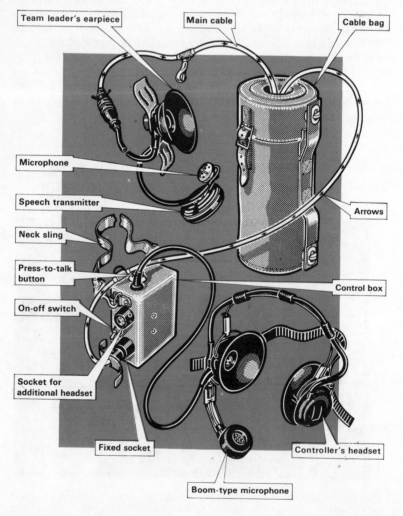

Fig. 6.4 The 'Southampton' breathing apparatus communications equipment

Fig. 6.4 shows the complete equipment which has only two switches, both operated by the controller. One is an on/off switch which is turned to the 'on' position at the commencement of use of the equipment, so that the line from the controller to the team leader is 'live' all the time, and the other is a 'press to talk' button used by the controller when he speaks to the team leader.

If it is necessary to extend the link beyond the length of the 300 ft (91 m) cable carried, additional cables may be connected. The maximum length of line recommended by the manufacturers is 900 ft (274 m).

c. The Diktron communications equipment

The Diktron equipment (Fig. 6.5) uses microphone and amplifiers as the means of communication. The amplifying unit is complete

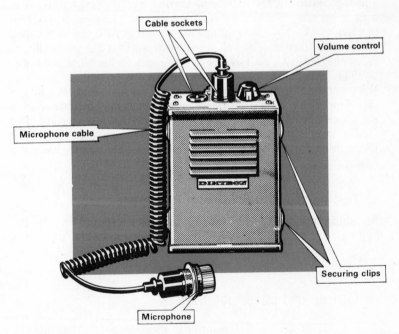

Fig. 6.5 The Diktron breathing apparatus communications equipment

with a special built-in rechargeable 12-volt battery for its power supply, and is sealed and recharged *in situ*. Only one control is fitted, i.e. a volume control on the built-in loudspeaker. This is located on the top panel of the amplifying unit. No switches are necessary as the amplifier becomes 'live' when the microphone connecting cable is inserted in its three-pin socket. The unit is about 6 ins by $4\frac{1}{2}$ ins by 2 ins ($152 \times 114 \times 51$ mm) and weighs about $4\frac{3}{4}$ lb (2·2 kg) with battery. Various carrying harnesses are available for the different types of breathing apparatus to which they are secured by snap hooks, generally at the front, but the unit may alternatively be carried on the right-hand side under the arm.

The face mask of the team leader is fitted with a microphone which, at the start of operations, is connected to the amplifying unit by means of a special cable having safety pull-out connectors; these allow the cable to pull away from the microphone in the event of it being caught up. The facility avoids the possibility of the mask being pulled away from the wearer's face.

As with the 'Southampton' equipment, communication between a team leader and the controller is by means of 300 ft (91 m) of cable marked with arrows. The cable is carried in a pvc-coated canvas container. The same type of unit is used by both the team leader and the controller, the unit being carried on the chest by means of a neck harness. The controller's microphone, however, is mounted in a half mask which prevents any extraneous noise being transmitted to the team leader. The half mask also prevents the possibility of 'acoustic feed-back', a howl developing due to the close proximity of microphone and speaker when high levels of volume are used. Where the ambient noise at the control is such that difficulty is experienced in receiving messages, headphones may be connected in the sockets provided, thereby muting the internal loudspeaker. This facility may also be used where privacy is required, when it is undesirable for onlookers to overhear messages coming over the loudspeaker.

d. Testing of communications equipment

Breathing apparatus communications equipment should be examined and tested in accordance with Test No. 3, (Section IV (1)), as detailed in the *Fire Service Drill Book*.

4 Guide and personal lines

Section III of the 'B A Operational Procedure' (*see* Chapter 12) requires at least one guide line to be carried on each appliance with breathing apparatus, and a personal line in a suitable container to be attached to each breathing apparatus set. The purpose of the guide line is to provide a means whereby the first team to enter and search a smoke-filled risk can retrace its steps, and to enable subsequent teams to make their way and return from the scene of operations with the minimum of difficulty. The personal line enables the wearer to attach himself to a guide line and follow it throughout

Plate 1. Proto Mark V 1-hour oxygen breathing apparatus with full face mask.

Plate 2. Rear view of the Proto Mark V set showing a guide-line carrier.

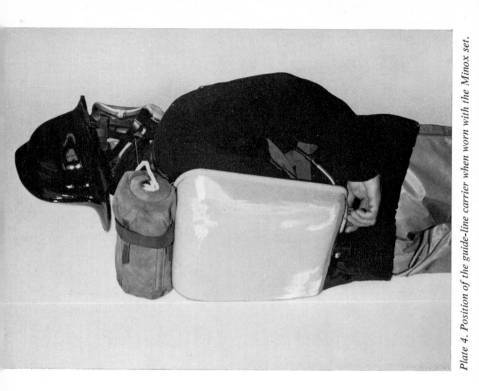

Plate 3. Front view of the Minox 1-hour oxygen breathing apparatus.

Plate 4. Position of the guide-line carrier when worn with the Minox set.

Plate 5. The Siebe Gorman 'Airmaster' compressed-air breathing apparatus.

Plate 6. Rear view of the 'Airmaster' set showing an ultra-lightweight cylinder and cover.

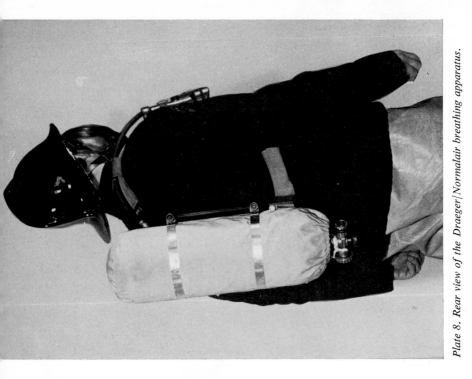

Plate 8. *Rear view of the Draeger/Normalair breathing apparatus.*

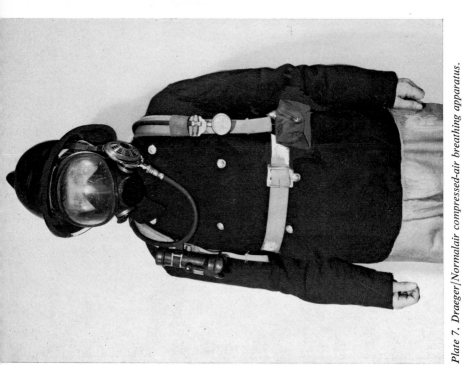

Plate 7. *Draeger/Normalair compressed-air breathing apparatus.*

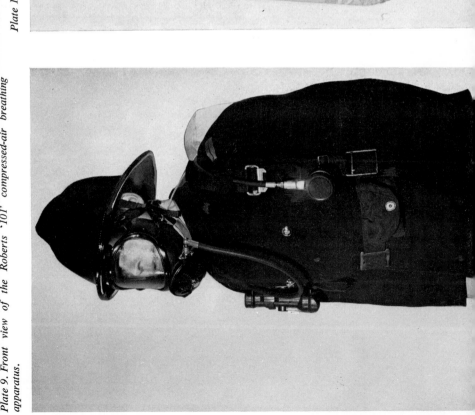

Plate 9. Front view of the Roberts '101' compressed-air breathing apparatus.

Plate 10. The Roberts '101' compressed-air set from the rear.

Plate 12. The Control Officer entering details on the Stage I B.A. Control board.

Plate 11. Breathing apparatus entry control procedure. Men handing in their tallies to the Stage I Control Officer.

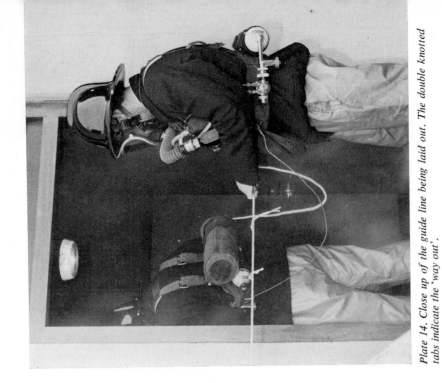

Plate 14. Close up of the guide line being laid out. The double knotted tabs indicate the 'way out'.

Plate 13. A Stage II B.A. Control in operation showing the men laying out a guide line.

Plate 16. Operators wearing communications equipment at a breathing apparatus incident.

Plate 15. Men wearing breathing apparatus being supplied by air-line equipment.

its length, and to search away from the guide line up to the limit of the personal line. A description of guide and personal lines is contained in the *Manual*, Book 2, 'Fire brigade equipment', in Chapter 11, 'Lines used in the fire service'.

Reference has been made to arrow markings on communication cables to indicate the way out to the control point. Such markings are not practicable on guide lines and so a special method of identifying them by touch has been devised. These markings are also detailed in Book 2, Chapter 11.

Chapter 7
Breathing apparatus cylinders

1 Design and specifications

Specification JCDD/19 (self-contained breathing apparatus for fire brigade use) lays down that cylinders for use with breathing apparatus must conform to current Home Office regulations for gas cylinders, or be of a design approved by the Home Office for the purpose. Cylinders must also be coloured in accordance with British Standard 1319, current edition.

The Gas Cylinders (Conveyance) Regulations (and subsequent Exemption Orders) set out, amongst other things, detailed requirements with regard to the construction and testing of cylinders, and no cylinder of a capacity to which the Regulations apply shall be used for the conveyance by road of any of the gases named in the Regulations (included are oxygen and air), that is not in accordance with one of the specifications contained therein. Nor may any cylinder that fails to pass the prescribed periodic tests be used for the conveyance of any gas to which the Regulations apply.

The original Regulations were made in 1931 and required cylinders to be of carbon steel with a working pressure of not more than 120 atmospheres (1800 lbf/in² (124 bars)). Subsequently an Exemption Order admitted cylinders of manganese steel, also with a maximum working pressure of 120 atmospheres. In July 1942 provisional regulations were made permitting the charging pressure of cylinders covered by the original regulations to be increased by 10 per cent, and in 1947 regulations were made authorising the 10 per cent increase as a permanent measure. Thus the permissible charging pressure for all carbon steel and manganese steel cylinders covered by the Regulations is now 132 atmospheres (1980 lbf/in² (136·5 bars)).*

Another Exemption Order, also made in 1947, permitted the use of alloy steel cylinders to Air Ministry or Ministry of Aircraft Production Specification No. 0.133. The alloy steel used for these cylinders had a much higher tensile strength than either carbon or manganese steel and in consequence the cylinder walls could be thinner and the cylinder itself was much lighter in weight. These cylinders were designed for a charging pressure of 120 atmospheres

* See footnote on page 25.

under normal conditions, but subsequently their use was extended to underwater work, and because this increased the possibility of corrosion, the cylinders were given a *corrosion allowance* by increasing the wall thickness by 10 per cent. Approval was then given for the charging pressure of cylinders with the 10 per cent corrosion allowance to be increased to 132 atmospheres, provided they were not to be used under water.

In 1962 two new specifications ('S' and 'T') for seamless alloy steel cylinders were issued by the Home Office. The second specification ('T') was for cylinders specifically for use with breathing apparatus where a lighter-weight cylinder was necessary. Cylinders to these specifications are not limited on charging pressure, in that the wall thickness of the cylinder is determined to suit any charging pressure for which the cylinder is designed. The consequence of these new specifications is that charging pressures of 200 atmospheres (3000 lbf/in² (207 bars))* have come into general use, and there is no restriction on the use of higher pressures if desired.

The Gas Cylinders (Conveyance) Regulations also prescribe that each cylinder must be subjected to a periodic inspection and hydraulic stretch test. The interval for the inspection and hydraulic test was originally specified as two years, but in 1959 this was increased to five years. Each cylinder is also required to bear the specification mark, the manufacturer's and owner's identification marks, the serial number of the cylinder and the date of the last hydraulic test. These requirements are also included in specifications 'S' and 'T'.

The Regulations apply only to cylinders with a water capacity of more than 12 lb (5·4 kg) and, strictly, only the cylinders of compressed-air sets fall within the Regulations. The water capacity of the cylinders supplied with existing compressed-air sets is about 20 lb (9 kg), whereas that of the 1-hour *Proto* set is less than 3 lb (1·4 kg). However, by common consent of all concerned, the provisions of the Regulations are applied to all breathing apparatus cylinders irrespective of size.

As a general guide it may be assumed that cylinders supplied with oxygen breathing apparatus prior to the introduction of Specification 'T' were made from carbon steel. Recently, alloy steel cylinders to Specification 'T' have been introduced with the object of reducing weight, even though the saving on these small cylinders is slight.

As regards compressed-air apparatus, cylinders supplied before the introduction of Air Ministry Specification No. 0.133 were probably of manganese steel and subsequently they would be to the Air Ministry specification until cylinders to Specification 'T' class came into use.

It is proposed to introduce new regulations to supersede the original regulations and Exemption Orders already mentioned. These

---

* See footnote on page 25.

new regulations will refer to a number of British Standards relating to pressure vessels which are at present in course of preparation and will cover both low as well as high pressure vessels and all sizes above 1 kg water capacity.

The aim of all concerned is to reduce the weight of breathing apparatus and to increase the duration of compressed-air sets. The cylinder represents a comparatively small proportion of the total weight of an oxygen apparatus, but the charged cylinder of the existing compressed-air sets represents about two-thirds of the total weight. Any appreciable saving in weight on compressed-air apparatus can, therefore, only be achieved by a reduction in the weight of the cylinder.

The question often asked is why cylinders for breathing apparatus are not made from aluminium alloy. Existing regulations do not permit the use of aluminium alloy cylinders, but there are Home Office specifications for aluminium alloy cylinders designed on similar principles to those of alloy steel. However, it may be of interest to examine the relative weights of aluminium and steel cylinders. Aluminium alloys with properties suitable for the manufacture of cylinders have a very much lower tensile strength than steels, and have about one-third of the tensile strength of the alloy steels used for cylinders to Specification 'T'. Thus, to provide the same strength the aluminium cylinder would have to have three times the wall thickness of the steel cylinder, and as aluminium is approximately one-third of the weight of steel, the weights of the two cylinders would be about the same. With steels of lower tensile strength, such as the original carbon and manganese steels, the use of aluminium alloy would have shown some saving in weight, but with steels of higher tensile strength as are now being widely used, steel cylinders will be appreciably lighter in weight than any aluminium cylinders of the same capacity.

In the early 1960s the use of much higher tensile steels, i.e. about one-and-a-half times the tensile strength of steels used for cylinders to Specification 'T', was considered and cylinders were produced for trials. The use of these higher tensile steels permitted much thinner walls and required special methods of manufacture to ensure that the cylinder walls were kept to their design thickness. Cylinders of this type are referred to by fire brigades as 'ultra-lightweight cylinders' because their weight when empty is only slightly more than the average 1240-litre cylinder to Specification 'T', yet they hold about 80 per cent more air. When charged the difference in weight between the two types of cylinder is more marked because the weight of the extra air in the ultra-lightweight cylinder is about 3 lb (1·36 kg). There are only two manufacturers of these cylinders at present, one of which makes a cylinder of welded construction (Specification LASW 1—light alloy steel welded) and the other a seamless cylinder (Specification LASS 1—light alloy seamless steel).

Cylinders to these specifications have received Home Office approval only for use by certain specified authorities (of which the fire service is one), and they will not be included at this stage in the new regulations referred to above. Also, for the time being at least, they are required to be inspected and tested at more frequent intervals than other types of cylinder used by fire brigades.

Because of the relatively thin walls of ultra-lightweight cylinders, it is most important to prevent corrosion, both internally and externally. The specifications call for special internal anti-corrosion treatment, but nevertheless it is necessary to prevent moisture from accumulating in the cylinders. For this reason it has been recommended that air used to charge the cylinders should have a dew point not higher than −50°C. To protect the outer surface of the cylinders, the use of protective covers has been advocated with, in addition, the regular 'touching up' of any damage to the paint.

2   Identification colours for cylinders

Gas cylinders are coloured for ease of identification, cylinders for gases used commercially being marked in accordance with British Standard 349, and those for medical gases in accordance with British Standard 1319. Cylinders for use with breathing apparatus are marked to BS 1319, the body of oxygen cylinders being black and the valve end, down to the shoulder, white. The body of air cylinders is grey, with the valve end down to the shoulder in black, and with white quarters. (*See* Plate No. 42 in Part 6C of the *Manual*, 'British Standard colours for medical gas cylinders'—Book 18 in the new format.)

3   Charging of cylinders

Cylinders should be charged to a pressure not exceeding the maximum working pressure, which is normally marked on the cylinder body. Cylinders are normally sent for charging to one of the companies having special charging facilities. Many fire brigades, however, have their own charging plant, which may be either a fixed electrically-driven compressor or a portable hand pump. Oxygen compressors and hand pumps have to be water-lubricated as oxygen causes rapid oxidation of oils and greases, and this in turn may cause spontaneous combustion.

Fixed electrically-driven compressors are capable of charging several cylinders at the same time, depending on the size of the compressor. It is important not to charge a cylinder too quickly as the rapid compression of the gas causes a rise in temperature. This will in turn cause a rise in pressure in the cylinder and on cooling the pressure will drop. The charging rate should, therefore, be controlled to prevent an undue rise in temperature, and if on cooling to room temperature the pressure drop in a cylinder is significant, it should be 'topped up'.

The supply of gas for oxygen compressors and for hand pumps is drawn from large cylinders. These should also be *medical* cylinders because although the purity of the gas supplied for medical and commercial purposes is generally the same, there is a slight possibility that commercial cylinders may be contaminated internally.

Fixed air compressors draw their air from the atmosphere and the air intake should always be taken from outside the building and be in a position well away from fumes or other possible source of contamination. Both air and oxygen compressors should contain adequate filters, purifiers and driers to ensure that, as far as possible, the gas delivered to the breathing apparatus cylinder is clean and dry.

Charging by hand pump is rather slow, particularly as the pressure in the supply cylinder drops, but it has an advantage in that it can be used for charging cylinders at a fire or other incident where breathing apparatus is used.

4 Care and maintenance of cylinders

Cylinder valves are an integral part of the cylinder and should not be removed. It may, however, sometimes be necessary to renew the valve seating or gland packing; this should be carried out in accordance with the maker's instructions.

Oils and greases must NOT be allowed to come into contact with the cylinder or valve parts. Outlet threads should be protected with a blank cap when the cylinder is not connected to the apparatus.

Chapter 8
Working duration of breathing apparatus

1 Full duration, working duration and safety margin

Mention has already been made of the duration of a breathing apparatus set when in use, but it is not possible to determine this duration with accuracy, because there are variable factors depending upon the circumstances in which the set is used. In the case of oxygen closed-circuit sets with a constant flow, the duration may be reduced by the use of the by-pass, but the effect from this cause is likely to be slight. In the case of compressed-air open-circuit sets, however, the duration can be affected quite considerably by the lung capacity of the wearer and the degree of work undertaken. It is therefore necessary to allow for wider variations in duration with compressed-air sets than with oxygen sets.

Reference is made below to *full duration*, *working duration* and *safety margin*, and definitions of these terms are as follows:

Full duration is the time a breathing apparatus is expected to last from the moment it is started up until the cylinder is exhausted.

Working duration is the time a breathing apparatus is expected to last from the time it is started up until the cylinder pressure is reached at which the low-cylinder-pressure warning device (i.e. the whistle) starts to operate.

Safety margin is the time from the moment the whistle starts to sound until the cylinder is exhausted.

In short: working duration = full duration − safety margin.

The duration of a breathing apparatus, whether oxygen or compressed air, depends on the quantity of oxygen or air in the cylinder and the average rate of consumption. It is usual to refer to the contents of a cylinder in litres and consumption in litres per minute and if, for example, the cylinder of an oxygen set contains 150 litres and the constant flow rating is 2·5 litres per minute, the *full duration* of the set will be

$$150 \div 2\tfrac{1}{2} = 150 \times \frac{2}{5} = 60 \text{ minutes.}$$

It has become the custom in the case of *Proto* sets to divide the cylinder pressure in atmospheres by two to find the duration of the set in minutes. This happens to work in the case of *Proto* sets because the cylinders were designed to be charged to 120 atmospheres, and $\frac{120}{2} = 60$, which is the generally accepted duration. Although this is convenient, it is applicable only to the *Proto* set with cylinders charged to 120 atmospheres. The present trend is to use higher charging pressures with a smaller cylinder. Thus instead of a cylinder charged to 120 atmospheres containing 150 litres, it might be charged to 200 atmospheres and contain the same amount, so that the duration would be the same in both cases. Clearly dividing the pressure of the smaller cylinder at 200 atmospheres by two would not give the correct duration in minutes.

It will be seen, therefore, that in order to provide for higher charging pressures it is necessary for a formula for the duration of sets to be based on the contents of the cylinder in litres and the rate of consumption in litres per minute. As stated earlier, the *working duration = full duration − safety margin*; it was also shown that the *full duration* is obtained by dividing the contents of the cylinder by the average rate of consumption.

It is therefore necessary now to consider how the contents of the cylinder, average rate of consumption and safety margin are to be obtained for any type of breathing apparatus.

2 Contents of cylinders

Information as to the quantity contained in cylinders when charged to the full charging pressure is obtainable from the manufacturers. The amount of the contents at any lower pressure can easily be determined because it is directly related to the pressure, i.e. three-quarters pressure—three-quarters contents; half pressure—half contents. The *Operational procedure for the use of breathing apparatus* states that a breathing apparatus is not normally to be used if a cylinder has less than five-sixths of its maximum contents, i.e. 100 atmospheres in the case of cylinders charged to 120 atmospheres and 165 atmospheres in the case of cylinders charged to 200 atmospheres.

3 Average rate of consumption

For oxygen sets with a constant flow, the average rate of consumption is taken as the constant flow setting; for example, $2\frac{1}{2}$ litres per minute for *Proto* sets. In the case of oxygen apparatus with a smaller constant flow augmented by a lung-governed valve, 2 litres per minute is taken as the average rate of consumption.

In the case of compressed-air sets the average rate of consumption is assumed to be 40 litres per minute, which is the average rate for a man walking at 4 miles per hour. Where a wearer undertakes exceptionally heavy work the rate may well be higher and the duration correspondingly less.

4 The safety margin

The safety margin recommended for all types of breathing apparatus is 10 minutes. In the case of 1-hour *Proto* sets, the whistle should be set to operate when the cylinder is at one-quarter pressure, i.e. when the cylinder is one-quarter full, so that theoretically the set still has 15 minutes to run. In fact, however, the whistle consumes nearly 2 litres per minute and so the actual safety margin is about 10 minutes. A corresponding allowance in the setting of the whistle will have to be made on all other oxygen sets in which the whistle discharges to atmosphere.

In the case of compressed-air sets, however, the loss of air due to the whistle is small compared with the rate of consumption and has a negligible effect on the remaining duration of the set; therefore no allowance need be made for the consumption of the whistle.

5 Calculating working duration

The formulae for determining the working duration of breathing apparatus sets are as follows:

a. Oxygen apparatus

$$\text{Working duration in minutes} = \frac{\text{Contents of cylinder in litres}}{\text{Constant flow (litres per minute)}} - 15.$$

NOTE: In the case of *Minox* breathing apparatus, it has already been stated that the working duration cannot be calculated as for other oxygen sets and has to be taken from the graph shown in Fig. 4.9. The working duration is therefore shown in Table 2.

b. Compressed-air apparatus

$$\text{Working duration in minutes} = \frac{\text{Contents of cylinder in litres}}{40} - 10.$$

c. Application of the formulae

Examples of the application of these formulae are given below:

(1) Proto 1-hour apparatus

Capacity of cylinder charged to 120 ats = 170 litres.

Working duration $= \dfrac{170}{2\frac{1}{2}} - 15$ $= 53$ minutes.

Capacity at 110 ats $= \dfrac{110}{120} \times 170$ $= 156$ litres.

Working duration $= \dfrac{156}{2\frac{1}{2}} - 15$ $= 47$ minutes.

Capacity at 100 ats $= \dfrac{100}{120} \times 170$ $= 142$ litres.

Working duration $= \dfrac{142}{2\frac{1}{2}} - 15$ $= 42$ minutes.

---

(2) Compressed-air apparatus

Capacity of cylinder charged to 132 ats = 1240 litres.

Working duration $= \dfrac{1240}{40} - 10$ $= 21$ minutes.

Capacity at 120 ats $= \dfrac{120}{132} \times 1240$ $= 1127$ litres.

Working duration $= \dfrac{1127}{40} - 10$ $= 18$ minutes.

Capacity at 110 ats $= \dfrac{110}{132} \times 1240$ $= 1033$ litres.

Working duration $= \dfrac{1033}{40} - 10$ $= 16$ minutes.

---

6 Working duration tables

Section 1 of the 'Operational Procedure' requires that working duration tables of breathing apparatus sets should be permanently marked on all B A Control boards. Tables 2 and 3 below include details of cylinders in use at the present time.

Table 2 *Oxygen apparatus*

Type	Cylinder capacity at maximum charging pressure	Cylinder pressure (atmospheres)	Working duration in minutes
Proto 1-hour	187 litres at 132 ats and 170 litres at 120 ats	132 120 110 100	60 53 47 42
Proto 2-hour	342 litres at 132 ats and 311 litres at 120 ats	132 120 110 100	122 110 99 89
Minox	360 litres at 170 ats	170 160 150 140	52 48 45 42

Table 3

Cylinder capacity at maximum charging pressure	Cylinder pressure (atmospheres)	Working duration in minutes
2250 litres at 200 ats (See Note 1)	200 190 180 170	46 43 40 38
1800 litres at 200 ats (See Note 1)	200 190 180 170	35 33 30 28
1200 litres at 200 ats (Non-standard 5½-in (140 mm) dia. cylinder—see Note 2)	200 190 180 170	20 18 17 15
1240 litres at 132 ats	132 120 110	21 18 16

NOTE 1. The 2250- and 1800-litre cylinders, which are both charged to the same pressure (200 atmospheres) but have different capacities, are interchangeable and serious consequences could result if the 2250-litre table was used for the 1800-litre cylinder. Where both types of cylinder are in use at the same incident, the duration table used must be that of the 1800-litre cylinder.

NOTE 2. This non-standard cylinder (diameter $5\frac{1}{2}$ ins (140 mm) instead of 7 ins (178 mm)) cannot be interchanged with others. To avoid confusion where different brigades are working at the same incident, it is recommended that the tally of sets with the non-standard cylinder should be given a distinctive marking in the form of a red diagonal line from the lower left to the upper right corner. The duration table on the control boards should be similarly marked.

Part 2
The operational use of breathing apparatus

Details of the various types of breathing apparatus in use by fire brigades, together with the reasons why it is necessary at times for firemen to wear breathing apparatus when working in oxygen-deficient and/or toxic atmospheres, have been given in Part 1. This Part is concerned with the operational use of breathing apparatus. The reader's attention, however, is also directed to the paragraphs on working and moving in smoke and darkness (*see* the *Manual*, Part 6A: pages 56–80, Book 11 in the new format), as the remarks made there are also relevant to those given in this Part, whether a fireman is equipped with breathing apparatus or not.

In order to provide adequate safeguards for men in breathing apparatus, the Secretary of State, on the advice of the Central Fire Brigades Advisory Council, has recommended an 'Operational Procedure for the use of breathing apparatus'. This 'Procedure' has been referred to briefly in Part 1 and is set out in detail in Chapters 10 to 12; the first part of the 'Procedure' deals with recording and supervising, the second with the communications procedure and the third with the use of guide and personal lines.

The 'Operational Procedure' as issued by the CFBAC is divided into three 'parts'. In order to avoid confusion with the 'Parts' into which this volume is divided, the 'Operational Procedure' parts have been shown as Section 1, Section 2 and Section 3.

Chapter 9
Working with breathing apparatus

It is important that every man who is required to wear breathing apparatus is not only adequately trained and thoroughly understands the 'Procedure' in all its aspects, but also that he faithfully and meticulously carries out the 'Procedure' at a fire or other incident, for on each member of the team or crew will depend the success of the operation in hand. It is not only a question of the man's own safety, but also that of his colleagues with whom he may be working at the time or subsequently. The success of breathing apparatus operations does not rest alone with those men working inside the building. It is not sufficient for men to be completely confident in their ability to work with breathing apparatus in hazardous conditions; they must also have full confidence that the control and support arrangements outside the building are beyond reproach. The whole success of any breathing apparatus job is team work, and it is incumbent on all those engaged in the operation to ensure that they are competent and fully conversant with their breathing apparatus and with the 'Procedure' for its use.

1. Wearing of breathing apparatus

Breathing apparatus is worn at a fire or other incident only on the instructions of the officer-in-charge who may, in fact, be a leading fireman or even a fireman in charge of the first appliance to arrive. The general principle should be that breathing apparatus is worn whenever its use will facilitate the location and extinction of a fire, or at any other incident when, by wearing breathing apparatus, discomfort and possible injury to a fireman's respiratory organs can be avoided.

The decision to order breathing apparatus to be worn will depend on a number of factors, such as the volume and type of smoke; whether the atmosphere is deficient of oxygen, is toxic or has a high temperature; the length of time men are likely to be exposed; or whether there is a hazard from radioactive substances.

As soon as instructions have been given for breathing apparatus to be worn, the officer-in-charge must nominate a B A Control Officer so that Stage 1 of the 'Procedure' can be put into operation. This is a simple act which need cause no delay as the control officer could be the pump operator who accepts the tallies from the wearers before they go in, having first made sure that the information required on the tallies, including the cylinder pressure, has been checked by the wearer when he dons his set, and is recorded on the tallies.

a. Precautions when donning breathing apparatus

The method of donning breathing apparatus and the sequence for starting up oxygen and compressed-air sets in general use by fire brigades, is detailed in the *Fire Service Drill Book* and need not be repeated here. For other types of set, the manufacturer's instruction books should be consulted.

Breathing apparatus must always be **donned and started up in fresh air,** and men standing by at a B A Control should make sure that they remain in fresh air until required. The practice of men rigging in fresh air but not putting on their face masks, or not putting in their mouthpieces, until they reach smoky atmospheres and then starting up their sets, **is extremely dangerous and must not be permitted.**

Only in most exceptional circumstances should an officer or man who has already inhaled smoke, oxygen deficient or toxic fumes, subsequently rig in breathing apparatus; the reason for this is that once smoke or toxic fumes are present in the lungs and respiratory passages, it takes an appreciable time for them to be completely cleared. If closed-circuit breathing apparatus particularly is donned after smoke has been inhaled, the smoke will be continually circulated and will cause irritation to the respiratory system and discomfort to the wearer. If carbon monoxide or other toxic fumes have been inhaled the continual circulation could have serious consequences.

When donning *Proto* breathing apparatus, care should be taken to ensure that the complementary strap is not too tight or that the breathing bag is not strapped too close against the body. When crawling in a confined space or when assuming a crouching position it is normally better to release the complementary strap and allow the bag to hang free; if the bag is not free in such circumstances it may be flattened or doubled up with the result that the oxygen may be forced out of the pressure relief valve, the face mask or mouthpiece, which besides wasting oxygen will cause discomfort to the wearer. When working in difficult and restricted conditions, care should be taken to ensure that the breathing tubes do not become kinked.

Reasonable care should be taken in the handling and movement of breathing apparatus at all times, particularly so with *Proto* apparatus, in order to prevent movement of the absorbent which could result in particles entering the valves or breathing tubes.

b. Removal of mouthpiece or face mask

The mouthpiece or face mask of a breathing apparatus set is designed to prevent any external atmosphere from entering the respiratory system, and it is exceedingly dangerous for the mouthpiece or face mask to be removed when the wearer is in a smoky or toxic atmosphere. Once the mouthpiece or face mask is removed, smoke, carbon monoxide or other toxic gases can enter the respiratory system and the conditions described above will be created to a dangerous degree. *If a mouthpiece, nose clip or face mask is dislodged whilst the wearer is in a smoky or toxic atmosphere, it is vital that the wearer should hold his breath and immediately replace the dislodged part.* If, for any reason, there is a likelihood of delay in doing so, the wearer should contact the other member(s) of his crew, and he should be accompanied to open air as quickly as possible, even though he may not feel any ill effect from the few breaths of contaminated air which he has been forced to inhale. The victim of carbon monoxide poisoning may not appreciate the presence of the gas until it is too late for him to call for assistance or to make his way out of the contaminated atmosphere.

c. Closing down

When a breathing apparatus wearer has completed his task and returns to normal atmosphere, the set should be closed down as follows:

(1) Full face mask

The headstraps should be slackened, the face mask removed and then the cylinder valve should be closed.

(2) With mouthpiece and nose clip

The goggles should be raised and then the nose clip and mouthpiece should be removed. The cylinder valve should then be closed.

2 Entering the building

a. General

If the incident is seen to be large or is likely to be protracted, Stage II of the 'Procedure' may be necessary before action is started. In such cases the officer-in-charge may decide to await reinforcements before committing men to work if his availability is inadequate at the time; for example, the officer-in-charge may decide that communications equipment, which might not be available on the first attendance, is necessary before the men enter the premises.

When plans of the building or hazard are available, they should be referred to as soon as possible, or if an occupant of the building who has a comprehensive knowledge of the layout of the building is present, he should be consulted. Any time devoted to consultation and study of the situation may result in a considerable saving of time and effort later.

Inside the building it may be found that visibility is extremely poor or non-existent due to lack of lighting (either daylight or artificial), because of smoke of varying density or colour, or because of fumes which are translucent. Lamps are always carried as part of breathing apparatus equipment, but even electric lamps may be of little or no use in heavy smoke conditions. No man should enter or be left alone in a building and the 'Procedure' requires that there must always be a minimum of two men working together.

When passing through compartments or corridors or negotiating stairs, breathing apparatus men should keep to the same side and avoid, where possible, crossing from one side to the other. This is particularly important if a guide line is being secured or a line of hose is being taken into a building as it will avoid confusion or difficulty to subsequent breathing apparatus crews.

b. Working by touch

Working in pairs engenders confidence, and contact should be maintained as far as possible by physical touch and by speaking when face masks with speech diaphragms are worn. When mouthpieces and tubes are used with breathing apparatus, speech between men should *not* be attempted. Trying to speak 'round the mouthpiece' is dangerous as smoke or toxic fumes could gain ingress.

When in strange surroundings and unable to see, the only course is to work by touch and to follow the elementary precautions of shuffling along with the feet and feeling with the back of the hand for obstructions. In this way any danger of bumping into obstructions or falling down openings in floors or stairways will be minimised. If the leading man halts for any reason, the men following will become aware of this by contact, and the reason for the halt should be communicated as far as possible to the others. This is easy when speech is possible but where speech between the men is not possible and the men following the leader need to halt (as may be necessary when a guide line or communication cable is being laid and secured), an effective method is for the man to give a single tap on the shoulder of the man in front. If some action is required, such as making fast a guide line, the action can be mimed or indicated by sense of touch. When all is ready for moving forward again, the man in front should be tapped twice on the shoulder to indicate readiness to proceed. Another method which can be used when a breathing apparatus man without speech facilities requires to draw attention to himself (for example, to obtain an indication of direction), is for the man to give intermittent loud *slow* hand claps. Whenever such handclapping is heard, the reason for this signal should be investigated by the remaining crew members.

3 Emergency procedure

a. Distress alarms

A distress signal warning device (Fig. 6.2) is provided with every breathing apparatus set in order that a breathing apparatus wearer who is in distress can summon assistance. These distress signal warning units should be carried in a standard position (Fig. 6.1) and it is recommended that they be carried on the right-hand side of the set, chest high, with the buzzer facing downwards.

In the unlikely event of a distress signal warning device failing to operate, the warning device of another member of the crew should be operated. When a distress signal warning is sounded, all men hearing the signal must go towards the sound of the signal. The rendering of assistance must take precedence over the work in hand, but due regard must be paid to keeping an escape route open, and once sufficient help is available to deal with the emergency, any branches temporarily abandoned must be got to work again with the minimum of delay.

b. Evacuation of premises

Although a standard evacuation signal of repeated short blasts on a whistle has been recommended by the Central Fire Brigades Advisory Council (*see* the *Manual*, Part 6A: page 73–Book 11 in the new format), such a signal cannot be operated by men wearing breathing apparatus, and evacuation instructions to crews would normally be given via the communications equipment, if in use. If men wearing breathing apparatus, however, hear repeated short blasts from a whistle, they should immediately make their way out of the premises.

c. Entrapped procedure

The object of the entrapped procedure is to enable a man to extend the duration of the breathing apparatus he is wearing in the event of his being trapped and unable to withdraw. In such circumstances, he should relax in as comfortable a position as possible, breathe shallowly and operate his distress signal warning device. If the low-cylinder-pressure warning whistle sounds, the air supply to it should be turned off where a valve is provided.

(1) Oxygen apparatus

These sets have a constant flow or a controlled flow of oxygen from the cylinder, and the entrapped procedure is to allow the breathing bag to fill and then to turn off the cylinder valve. If a man is unconscious or trapped in such a way as to prevent him operating the controls of his set, it should be done for him by another man, if he is in a position to do so. When the oxygen in the circuit has been consumed, the cylinder valve is opened again and the procedure repeated. For sets fitted with an automatic relief valve, it is important to allow the bag to fill only to the point at which the relief valve operates.

The entrapped procedure, when applied correctly to oxygen sets, can extend the duration of a fully-charged cylinder for several hours.

(2) Compressed-air apparatus

As these sets function on the 'demand' principle, no operation of the controls is necessary on the part of the wearer. A man would, therefore, be protected for a prolonged period even if he were unconscious. The procedure to be followed is simply to breathe as shallowly as possible in order to reduce the consumption of air. When completely relaxed, consumption of air may be reduced to about 10 litres a minute, which is about one-quarter of the average consumption.

4 Line signals

There may be occasions when a fireman wearing breathing apparatus has to be lowered down a shaft or sewer to effect a rescue or for other reasons, and some means of communication should be provided. Breathing apparatus communications equipment would be perfectly suitable, and in some cases, such as in cliff rescues, radio or even loud hailers may be used; these, however, do not allow both hands to be free at all times, which is usually essential for cliff rescues. As an alternative, or where breathing apparatus communication equipment is not available, recourse may be made to line signals.

The following signals should be employed:

Signal on line	Given by wearer	Given by attendant
1 pull	I am all right	Are you all right?
2 pulls	Pay out more line.	I am paying out more line.
2 pulls—pause—2 pulls	Stop lowering.	I am ceasing lowering.
3 pulls	Haul in slack line, or Haul up.	I am hauling in slack line, or I am hauling up.
Repeated, sharp pulls	Danger—help me out.	Danger—I am hauling up as quickly as possible.

In every instance when line signals are employed, they should be acknowledged by the recipient of the order repeating the signal to show that it has been understood and is being acted upon.

5 Working in high expansion foam

Because high expansion foam is opaque, visibility in it is nil; also the audibility of speech between breathing apparatus operators when using speech diaphragms may be reduced. In addition, the intensity of the low-cylinder-pressure warning whistle and the warning signal emitted by the distress signal unit is reduced, so there is a need for even greater control when breathing apparatus men have to enter high expansion foam.

Immersion in high expansion foam may, therefore, give a feeling of complete isolation because sounds are virtually inaudible and reports have indicated that firemen may experience psychological effects similar to claustrophobia much more strongly than in smoke. Men should always maintain physical touch with each other and full use should be made of the safeguards provided by guide lines and communications equipment which embodies earpiece facilities.

6   Working in special gases or vapours

The safety of breathing apparatus wearers depends, of course, upon much more than the efficiency of their sets. It is essential that they should have complete confidence in their sets and in their own ability to cope with all conditions they are likely to encounter in practice. This can only be achieved by thorough basic and regular continuation training.

There are, of course, certain aspects of instruction and training which cannot very well be demonstrated by practical trials. For example, special care is necessary if breathing apparatus is to be used in trichlorethylene vapour. This substance is a non-flammable toxic liquid used in industry as a solvent and degreasing agent. It is a powerful rubber solvent and trichlorethylene vapour will, in time,

Fig. 9.1 Ammonia suit worn with breathing apparatus

penetrate rubber parts of a breathing apparatus. It is essential, there-fore, that breathing apparatus should not be worn for longer periods than are absolutely necessary in an atmosphere containing this vapour.

Hydrogen cyanide is another substance which is extremely dan-gerous, as it can be absorbed through the skin, and so special pre-cautions are necessary. Special precautions are also necessary for ammonia gas which, in strong concentrations, causes acute irritation of the skin, particularly those parts of the body which are wet or covered with sweat. For this reason, special protective clothing (Fig. 9.1) is often worn with breathing apparatus when dealing with incidents involving ammonia.

7 Working in hot and humid atmospheres

There are a number of factors which may affect the upper tolerance limits for men at work in hot conditions; the most important of these are dry bulb temperature,* wet bulb temperature,* air movement, clothing and duration of exposure. Professor Haldane as long ago as 1905 concluded that wet bulb temperature was the most important single factor limiting a man's ability to withstand heat. It will be seen, therefore, that the worst atmospheric conditions for working are high temperatures associated with high humidity and lack of air movement. Such conditions can build up over a period of time, but it is unlikely that these conditions would occur at fires attended by fire brigades in the United Kingdom. A limited degree of humidity may arise from the combustion of materials containing substantial amounts of water, and of course the humidity will rise when a fire is first attacked with jets of water, but this will also bring down the temperature and create air movement.

In fire situations where there is a lack of ventilation, such as in basements, ships' holds, etc., high temperatures will be encountered, and the length of time men will be able to work in them will be governed by the actual amount of physical effort required, the men's ability to withstand heat and not the working duration of the breath-ing apparatus. Under such conditions, provision must be made to relieve the men at frequent intervals; in extreme cases reliefs at 15-minute intervals may be required.

There is a considerable variation in individual response to heat which may not necessarily bear any relation to the man's physical

---

*A measure of humidity of the atmosphere. A pair of similar thermometers are mounted side by side, one having its bulb wrapped in a damp wick dipping in water. The rate of evaporation of the water from the wick, and the consequent cooling of the 'wet bulb', is dependent on the relative humidity of the air. The amount of humidity can be obtained by means of a table from the readings of the two thermometers.

fitness or his ability to perform the task. The following is a brief outline of the effects of heat on the human body.

The human body is normally constantly generating heat, and surplus heat is dispelled through the skin and by ventilation through the lungs. If the temperature rises in the body due, for example, to exertion or to high ambient temperature, it is dispelled by sweat, which has a cooling effect on the skin as it dries; also some 10 per cent of body heat is dispelled through the lungs, i.e. in exhaled breath. The normal body temperature is about 37°C, and if a man is unable to get rid of the heat he generates through exertion or other reason, the body temperature will rise. If the temperature rises much above 39°C, symptoms similar to those experienced when one has a fever will develop, which will lead to lassitude and lightheadedness. If the temperature rises still further to about 41°C, the man will become unconscious. The rate at which heat can be dispelled from the body is, of course, slower in hot than in cold conditions, and in hot conditions it is slower if the temperature is humid than if it is dry.

Under hot and humid conditions the moisture in the air makes it more difficult to get rid of body heat because it prevents the evaporation of sweat and the exhalation of moisture and consequent heat from the lungs. For this reason it is desirable that breathing apparatus sets provide so far as possible cool air to breathe, and this is why a cooler is fitted to the regenerative apparatus.

Hot and humid atmospheres are encountered in mines because of the presence of inherent moisture and water together with a lack of ventilation. This condition is, of course, aggravated by fire, and the National Coal Board have had a great deal of research carried out to establish working times for mines rescue teams under varying conditions. Some information about this research may be of interest.

Extensive tests have been carried out at the Mines Rescue Station, Doncaster, and the Department of Human Anatomy at Oxford University, as a result of which conclusions have been reached as to the safe working times for men wearing breathing apparatus in conditions similar to those of the tests. The work routine at the Mines Rescue Station was designed to represent a mines rescue task, and two types of breathing apparatus were used: the *Proto* and a liquid air set, which, as would be expected, generally gave slightly better results than the oxygen gas set. The men were in two age groups, i.e. 19 to 31 years and 39 to 45 years of age, and the Doncaster tests indicated that there was no effect upon 'tolerance time' due to age; the men of the older group continued to work for as long as the men of the younger group.

The results of the tests show that rescue men wearing *Proto* breathing apparatus may be expected to work in saturated air environments for about 60 minutes when the saturated temperature is 27°C and 19 minutes when the saturated temperature is 38°C. With a dry bulb temperature of 38°C and a wet bulb temperature of 31°C a working time with *Proto* apparatus of 56 minutes was observed. Where the dry bulb temperature was 49°C and the wet bulb temperature was 26°C, the working time was about 55 minutes. The working times at these temperatures were slightly longer when the liquid air sets were used because these sets allow men to breathe cool, dry air.

These figures suggest that firemen wearing breathing apparatus may be able to work in conditions similar to those of the tests for up to one hour. With lower wet bulb temperature, somewhat high dry bulb temperatures could be withstood or longer periods of work undertaken. The normal operational duration of breathing apparatus in use by fire brigades is within the hour, and if men work for the full duration of their sets they should always be rested before they are required to undertake further work.

It should be borne in mind, however, that the working times arrived at as a result of the National Coal Board research are only applicable where the conditions, including the work rate, are the same as those used for the tests. The results should, therefore, be taken as a broad guide only, as fire-fighting conditions may differ considerably from those of the tests. The working times of men wearing breathing apparatus should be determined solely by the conditions obtaining at the time, and as already stated, 15 minutes' working may not be excessive in certain situations under severe conditions.

Chapter 10
Operational procedure—Section I
Recording and supervising procedure

In addition to a thorough knowledge of breathing apparatus and its capabilities, it is necessary to provide wearers with adequate safeguards when the equipment is in operational use. As has already been stated, the Central Fire Brigades Advisory Council has recommended an 'Operational Procedure for the use of breathing apparatus'. This chapter deals with Section I, the recording and supervising procedure.

1 Introduction

The efficient operation of the 'Procedure' is based on the provision with each breathing apparatus set of an identification tally (Fig. 10.1) which will have marked upon it the following information:

    (1) name of brigade
    (2) station
    (3) type of apparatus
    (4) number of apparatus.

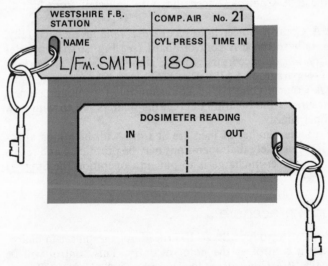

Fig. 10.1 Identification tally for use with breathing apparatus, to which is kept attached the key of the distress signal warning device. The reverse side of the tally makes provision for recording dosimeter readings at incidents involving radioactive substances

In addition, space will be provided for:
(5) name of wearer
(6) cylinder pressure
(7) time in.

One of these breathing apparatus tallies will be attached to the key of the distress signal warning device of each set.

After roll call, or as necessary at other times during each watch, men detailed to wear breathing apparatus are to check their sets and complete the information on the tallies. In the case of part-time retained men, this may be done *en route* to a fire, by the B A Control Officer at the fire, or as otherwise directed.

At least one guide line for use with breathing apparatus is to be carried on each appliance and every breathing apparatus man is to carry a personal line which he can clip on to the main guide line.

The 'Procedure' is divided into two stages. Stage I is to apply in all cases where breathing apparatus is used, and Stage II is to be introduced at the discretion of the officer-in-charge when the scale of operations demands a greater degree of control and supervision.

2 Stage I procedure

On giving instructions for breathing apparatus to be used, the officer-in-charge is to nominate a man as 'Control Officer'.

Each breathing apparatus wearer, before entering, is to check the cylinder pressure and the other details on the tally. He is to hand his tally to the B A Control Officer and is to collect it from him on leaving.

The B A Control Officer is to record the '*time in*' on each tally, attach the tally to the B A control board (*see* Fig. 10.2) and enter the '*time of whistle*' according to the standard tables of working duration (*see* paragraph 5 (*d*)—page 116).

The B A Control Officer is to be responsible for initiating emergency measures if the breathing apparatus wearers fail to withdraw at the proper time.

Where a large number of men are at work with breathing apparatus, or it seems likely that operations may be protracted and reliefs required, the officer-in-charge is to put into operation the Stage II Procedure.

3 Stage II procedure

On deciding to introduce Stage II Procedure, the officer-in-charge is to set up a control at the point of entry. This control will be known as the 'B A Control—Stage II' and a 'B A Control Officer is to be appointed to take charge of it.

If the situation demands more than one point of entry, a Stage II Control is to be set up and a control officer appointed for each point of entry. In these circumstances a 'Main Control' is also to be set up (*see* paragraph **(b)** below). Each control point should be marked in a distinctive way.

Each Stage II Control is to be provided with a control board (*see* Fig. 10.3) to which are to be attached the tallies of all breathing apparatus men operating from the control. The following additional information is to be recorded on the board in respect of each tally:

(1) time of whistle;

(2) location of teams (where appropriate). Any additional particulars, e.g. reliefs, are to be inserted in the 'Remarks' column.

A control officer will be responsible for a maximum number of 12 men. These could comprise six teams of two men per team, or fewer teams of more men. (A team will normally consist of two men and, other than in exceptional circumstances, will not exceed four men.)

If more than 12 men are to be committed simultaneously, an additional control officer is to be appointed for each subsequent group of up to 12 men (i.e. in excess of 12, 24, 36, etc.). Additional control boards are to be set up as necessary. Each control officer is to supervise the men for whom he is responsible until they have all withdrawn.

Each breathing apparatus wearer, before entering, is to hand his tally to the B A Control Officer, and is to collect it from him on leaving.

The tallies of men already at work under Stage I procedure are to be transferred to the appropriate Stage II control board by the Stage I Control Officer, who will then relinquish his responsibilities as directed.

a. Responsibilities of the Control Officer

The Stage II Control Officer's responsibilities are:

(1) To ensure that men are relieved at the appropriate time according to the record.

(2) To have sufficient men standing by for relief purposes at least five minutes before reliefs are due.

(3) To have at least two men standing by rigged with breathing apparatus for emergency purposes throughout the time the Control is operating.

(4) To initiate emergency measures when necessary, e.g. when men who are due out fail to report.

NOTE: Duty (3) will be the responsibility of the B A Main Control when one is in operation (*see* paragraph **(b)** below).

111

b. B A Main Control

Where more than one Stage II Control is set up, or where only one Stage II Control is operating and the number of men using it is likely to be large, an additional control to coordinate breathing apparatus requirements is to be set up. This control will be known as the 'B A Main Control'.

The B A Main Control is to be set up at the most convenient site for easy access and communication with all Stage II Controls. A control unit, emergency tender, or other suitable vehicle, may be used as the control.

An officer is to be nominated as 'Main Control Officer'. He is to take charge of the control and be responsible for all breathing apparatus requirements.

c. Duties of the B A Main Control

The duties of the B A Main Control Officer are:

(1) To meet requirements of Stage II Controls in manpower, breathing apparatus and other equipment. For this purpose a record is to be maintained of the relief requirements of each Stage II Control (*see* Fig. 10.4).

(2) To have available an adequate number of men rigged in breathing apparatus as reliefs, and to order them to Stage II Controls in time to enable these controls to carry out their responsibility indicated in paragraph (a) (2) above.

(3) To have at least two men standing by rigged with breathing apparatus for emergency purposes throughout the time the control is operating. This will relieve Stage II Controls of their responsibility indicated in paragraph (a) (3) above. If, however, the Main Control is far from the Stage II Control, the men should stand by at the Stage II Control.

(4) To arrange for sufficient absorbent, fully-charged cylinders and disinfectant to be available to meet requirements, and to prepare apparatus for re-use.

d. General

When they withdraw, breathing apparatus men, after collecting their tallies from the Stage II Control, are to report to the B A Main Control, if one is in operation.

For the B A Main Control to operate, communications are required with each Stage II Control. For this purpose, radio pack sets, messengers or telephones are to be used according to the facilities available.

4 Procedure to be followed by crews

Wearers of breathing apparatus are to adhere strictly to the following rules:

(1) At the commencement of operations, a breathing apparatus set is NOT to be used if the cylinder has less than five-sixths of its maximum contents.

> NOTE: This rule may be relaxed at the discretion of the B A Control Officer for men effecting a re-entry for a specific task.

(2) Breathing apparatus is only to be worn on the instructions of the officer-in-charge.

(3) Breathing apparatus must be donned in fresh air.

(4) Men are to work in teams of at least two. No man is to be left alone at work.

(5) Whenever a member of a team has to withdraw for any reason, e.g. if the withdrawal time of the team member with the shortest duration is reached, or in the event of accident, injury or illness affecting a team member, the *whole team must withdraw*.

(6) When a distress signal warning device is sounded, all men hearing the alarm are to make their way towards the sound of the signal. The rendering of assistance is to take precedence over the work in hand.

(7) Guide lines are to be used only on the instructions of the officer-in-charge.

(8) Men are not to enter a building without depositing their tallies with a B A Control Officer, and on leaving they must report to the control and collect their tallies. There should be a separate record to each re-entry.

5 Notes on the 'Operational Procedure'

a. Tallies

Coloured tallies have been adopted for different types of breathing apparatus to reduce the chances of the control officer referring to the wrong column of the tables of working duration which are similarly coloured, namely:

Oxygen	Over 90 minutes	Pink
	45–90 minutes	White
	Up to 45 minutes	Blue
	Minox	Green

Compressed air	Standard cylinders	Yellow
	Non-standard cylinders (*see* Note 2, page 96)	Yellow with red diagonal line
	Air-line	Yellow

b. Control boards – Stage I

A Stage I control board (Fig. 10.2) is to be carried on all appliances equipped with breathing apparatus, unless Stage II boards are carried instead (*see* paragraph **(c)** below).

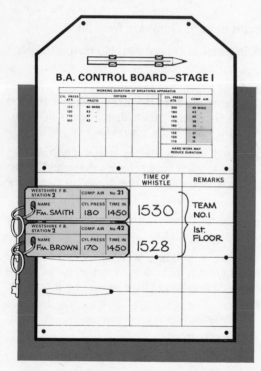

Fig. 10.2 The standard Stage I control board. A clock is fitted at the top of these boards if one is not otherwise available, e.g. on the appliance. The working duration tables should cover the types of set carried on the appliance

Consideration was given to having a combined nominal roll board and breathing apparatus control board, but this was rejected on the grounds that the two boards fulfil entirely different functions. The former carries the names of all members of the crew whereas the latter records only the names of breathing apparatus wearers.

It has been suggested that Stage I procedure may cause delays under certain circumstances. It is, however, necessary to operate Stage I procedure under all circumstances as it is particularly important that first attendance crews are safeguarded. This need not cause delay because breathing apparatus wearers have only to hand their tallies to the nominated breathing apparatus control officer (e.g. the pump operator), who has to attach them to the control board and record the times.

c. Control boards – Stage II

The standard Stage II control board is shown in Fig. 10.3. These boards should preferably be designed to take 12 tallies in order to facilitate the Stage II procedure as described on page 111. It may be convenient to hinge the lower half of the board so that it can fold up and cover the upper half when not in use. This has the advantage of protecting the clock face.

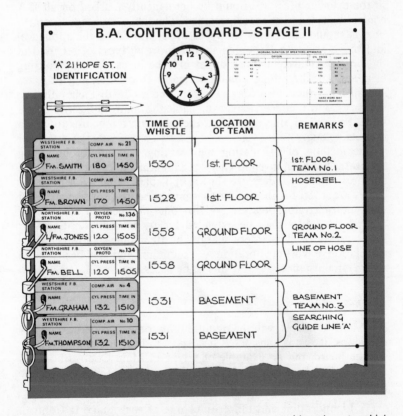

Fig. 10.3 A standard Stage II breathing apparatus control board, on to which the tallies shown on the Stage I board in Fig. 10.2 have been transferred

Stage II control boards may be carried on control units, emergency tenders or on other appliances to suit the fire brigade organisation. If desired, Stage II control boards may be carried instead of Stage I boards on all appliances carrying breathing apparatus.

When Stage II procedure is introduced, it is important that the clock on the control board agrees with the clock used for Stage I procedure. Unless there are arrangements within the brigade that all clocks are checked at regular intervals, the clock on the Stage II control board must be checked against, and if necessary set to agree with, the clock used for the Stage I procedure.

Stage II control boards should be sited in a prominent position near each point of entry, preferably rigidly mounted, e.g. on a searchlight tripod, but the method of mounting is optional.

d. Working duration tables

Tables giving the working duration of breathing apparatus according to the cylinder pressure should be permanently marked on all B A control boards in the space provided. The tables on Stage I control boards should cover only the types of set carried on the appliance, and those on Stage II boards should show all types of set used in the brigade. Different types of set may be in use in neighbouring brigades, and breathing apparatus teams from adjoining brigades should hand their own Stage I control boards with their tallies to the B A Control Officer. This will enable the control officer to determine the working durations from the tables on the boards to which the sets belong.

The method of calculating the working duration of breathing apparatus has been given in Chapter 8 and the tables for oxygen and compressed-air cylinders are shown in Tables 2 and 3 on page 95. Times are given for maximum charging pressures, for five-sixths of maximum charging pressure and for one intermediate pressure. If desired the tables may be extended locally to give durations for lower pressures. The safety margin of 10 minutes allowed in the calculation of working durations is a minimum and may be increased where circumstances suggest this to be necessary.

e. Main Control boards

As Main Controls will be required on only comparatively few occasions, it is not considered necessary to have a standard design for the board, but an example of a type of Main Control board is shown in Fig. 10.4. The Main Control board should, however, make provision for the following information:

(1) Identification and officer-in-charge of each Stage II Control.

(2) Number of reliefs required at each Stage II Control.

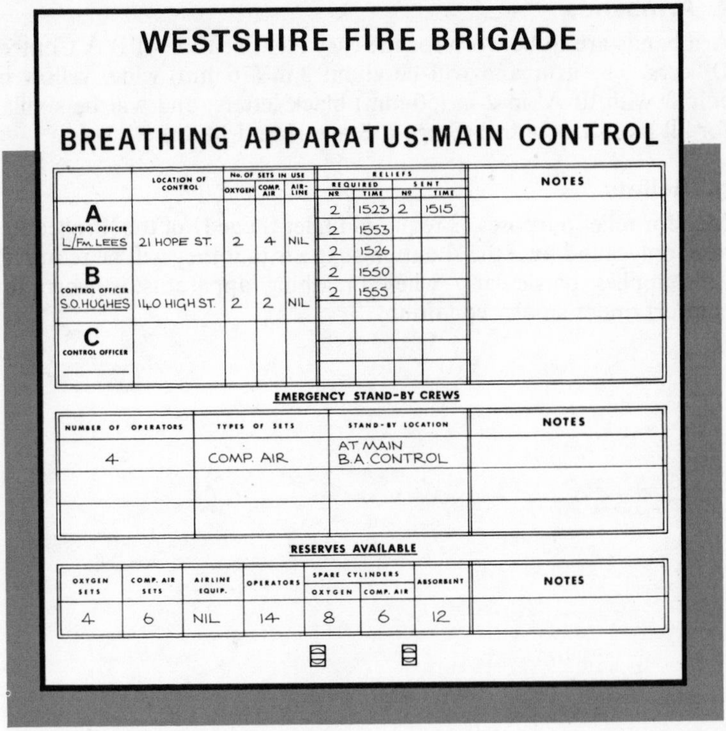

WESTSHIRE FIRE BRIGADE

BREATHING APPARATUS-MAIN CONTROL

LOCATION OF CONTROL		No. OF SETS IN USE			RELIEFS				NOTES
		OXYGEN	COMP. AIR	AIR-LINE	REQUIRED Nº	TIME	SENT Nº	TIME	
A CONTROL OFFICER L/Fm. LEES	21 HOPE ST.	2	4	NIL	2	1523	2	1515	
					2	1553			
					2	1526			
B CONTROL OFFICER S.O HUGHES	140 HIGH ST.	2	2	NIL	2	1550			
					2	1555			
C CONTROL OFFICER									

EMERGENCY STAND-BY CREWS

NUMBER OF OPERATORS	TYPES OF SETS	STAND-BY LOCATION	NOTES
4	COMP. AIR	AT MAIN B.A. CONTROL	

RESERVES AVAILABLE

OXYGEN SETS	COMP. AIR SETS	AIRLINE EQUIP.	OPERATORS	SPARE CYLINDERS OXYGEN	COMP. AIR	ABSORBENT	NOTES
4	6	NIL	14	8	6	12	

Fig. 10.4 The type of Main Control board which is used at the Fire Service Technical College. This will record the information shown on all Stage II Control boards in use

(3) Time at which reliefs are required and sent.

(4) Number and types of breathing apparatus set and operators available (excluding any in actual use), and particulars of spare cylinders and absorbent.

(5) Number of sets in use at each Stage II Control.

(6) Special notes relating to Stage II Controls. (Ample space should be left in this column.)

Unless the Main Control board is used where a clock is available, e.g. in a Control Unit, a separate clock should be provided on the board. Any clock used with a Main Control board must be synchronised with the clocks on Stage II control boards when the Main Control is brought into use.

f. Armbands

Armbands are to be worn for the easy identification of B A Control Officers. The armband will be about 3 in (76 mm) wide, yellow in colour with 'B A' in 2-in (50-mm) black letters, and will be similar for all levels of control (Stage I, Stage II and Main).

g. Reliefs

Men for relief purposes as required under Stage II of the 'Procedure' need only stand by if the situation suggests that they will be required. This applies particularly when breathing apparatus is worn for comfort under smoky conditions.

Chapter 11
Operational procedure—Section II
Communications procedure

1 Introduction

This communications procedure is to be put into operation as directed by the officer-in-charge at fires or special services when the situation requires a continuous communications link between a B A Control and the leader of a breathing apparatus team. The officer-in-charge of the B A Control (or a man nominated by him) is to wear speech reception and transmission equipment (*see* Chapter 6) connected by cable carried and paid out by the team leader, who is also to be equipped for speech reception and transmission.

2 The communications procedure

(a) On deciding to introduce the communications procedure, the officer-in-charge of the fire or special service is to give the necessary instructions to the officer-in-charge of the B A Control.

(b) The B A Control Officer, or a man nominated by him, is to don the control equipment.

(c) The leader of the breathing apparatus team, which may consist of two or more men, is to wear with his breathing apparatus a face mask with a speech diaphragm for communication with the other members of his team, a microphone for transmitting messages and an earpiece or amplifier for receiving messages. In addition, he is to carry in a container at least 300 ft (91 m) of cable which pays out automatically as he proceeds. Before leaving the B A Control, he is to connect the cable to the B A Control Officer's equipment and make a test call. If no hose or guide line is already laid out and if the team is not taking in a line of hose, the cable may be used as a guide line (*see* Section III of the 'Operational Procedure', Chapter 12).

(d) The team leader is to maintain continuous communication with the B A Control, reporting progress and, if the need arises, is to request assistance, e.g. additional breathing apparatus teams, hose, etc.

(e) The leaders of any additional breathing apparatus teams ordered in and working in the same general area are not to carry communications equipment, but are to rely on the original team leader for the transmission of messages.

(f) When the original team is to be relieved, the leader of the relief team is to wear the communications equipment described in (c) above, except that he is not to carry the cable. He is to test his equipment with the B A Control Officer and the team is then to proceed to the working position using the existing cable as a guide line (unless a separate guide line has already been laid out when they are to use the guide line). On arrival, the leader is to take over the cable container from the previous leader and is to connect his equipment to the cable. He is then to make a test call to the B A Control. The relieved crew is then to withdraw, using the cable as a guide line (or the guide line, if laid).

(g) If the original team have to withdraw before being relieved, the leader is to notify the B A Control Officer that the team is withdrawing and that communications will be discontinued. He is then to remove the cable carrier from his set, disconnect the cable and make it fast. The team is then to withdraw, using the cable as a guide line (or the guide line, if laid).

(h) In the event of a breakdown in communications, the following action is to be taken:

(1) The officer-in-charge of the B A Control is to inform the officer-in-charge of the fire. He is also to take steps to determine the cause of the breakdown by sending in the two men standing by for emergency purposes in accordance with Section I of the 'Operational Procedure', paragraph 3 (a) (3).

(2) The team leader is to use his discretion in deciding whether to withdraw his team immediately or to continue operations.

3 Notes on the communications procedure

It will be noted that the 'Procedure' deals only with communications between the team leader and the B A Control Officer. Members of the team may wear either face masks or mouthpieces with nose clips, but face masks fitted with speech diaphragms have the advantage of permitting communication between wearers.

When a communications team is making a reconnaisance, any information of special difficulties or obstructions, and also where there are no obstructions, should be passed to the control officer. This information should be given to men following the route later, whether or not a guide line is in use, as it will considerably speed progress. Similarly, when a communication cable is not laid, as much information as possible about the route should be given to the control officer by the men when they return.

Chapter 12
Operational procedure—Section III
Procedure for the use of guide and
personal lines

1 General

The use of guide lines is at the discretion of the officer-in-charge of a fire. It may be unnecessary to use them in residential type properties or known small basements and in cases where hose, hose reel hose or communications cable are laid by the first team to enter. They should, however, normally be used where premises are flooded, or are likely to be flooded, and hose lines are submerged.

The purpose of a guide line is to provide a means whereby the first team or crew to enter and search a smoke-filled risk can retrace its steps, and to enable subsequent teams to proceed to the scene of operations and return as necessary without difficulty.

The term 'guide line' means a special line which may be used either as a 'main guide line' for initial search and to indicate a route between a B A Control and the scene of operations, or, alternatively, as a 'branch guide line' when it is necessary to traverse or search deeply off a main guide line. The method of use of the line for either purpose is the same.

The term 'personal line' means a special line secured to the wearer of a breathing apparatus set, and which may be attached to a guide line to enable the wearer to follow the line and to search off it up to the limit of the personal line.

When following a guide line into an incident, a 4 ft (1·22 m) length of the personal line is usually most suitable, and this is referred to as a 'short personal line'.

2 Guide lines

a. Type and terminations

Guide lines should be between $\frac{3}{4}$-in (19 mm) and 1-in (25 mm) circumference hawser laid or plaited line, 200 ft (61 m) in length.

The running end should be fitted with a snap hook, smaller and different from the snap hook on the personal line, but sufficiently large to hook on to the guide line. The other end should terminate in a loop 6 ins (152 mm) in length. Guide lines are described and illustrated in Book 2 of the *Manual*, Chapter 11, 'Lines used in the fire service'.

b. Means of identifying the line when in use

To identify by touch the 'way out', two tabs 6 ins (152 mm) apart are to be fitted at 8-ft (2·44 m) intervals along the length of the line. One tab is to have two separate knots and an overall length of 2 ins (51 mm) and the other is to be unknotted and be 5 ins (127 mm) long. *The knotted tab is to be on the 'way out' side of the plain tab*, i.e. nearer to the running end of the line which is fitted with the snap hook. Nylon cord about $\frac{1}{8}$-in (3 mm) in diameter is suitable for these markings.

c. Guide line container

The line is to be carried in a fabric cylindrical container. The looped end of the line is to be attached to a snap hook inside the container. The line may be paid into the container in 'haphazard' fashion with the running end arranged to pay out from one end of the container, which should be carried on the back of the wearer. If the container is carried in an upright position, the line should preferably pay out from the top.

d. Extension of a guide line

A guide line can be extended by removing the looped end from the container and clipping the snap hook of another line on to the loop.

e. Number and designations of guide lines

(1) Only one main guide line is to be laid along a route from a B A Control to the scene of operations. Not more than two main guide lines are to be under the control of a B A Control Officer.

(2) Main guide lines are to be designated alphabetically by the letters 'A' and 'B' by means of circular tallies (Figs. 12.1, *left*), 3 ins

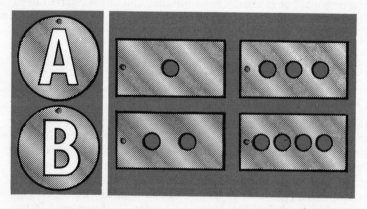

Fig. 12.1 Guide line designating tallies. Left: alphabetical tallies for main guide lines. Right: numerical tallies for identifying branch guide lines

(76 mm) in diameter, attached to the lines when they are secured at the control point. The letters should be not less than 2 ins (51 mm) in height. Two of these tallies, one marked 'A' and the other marked 'B', are to be carried with each B A Stage II control board.

(3) Branch guide lines are to be designated numerically by means of rectangular tallies (Fig. 12.1 *right*), 4×2 ins (102×51 mm) in size, with one, two, three or four $\frac{5}{8}$-in (16 mm) holes in them to indicate the number of the branch line. One set of four of these tallies are to be carried with each B A Stage II control board.

3 Personal lines

Personal lines should be about $\frac{1}{2}$-in (13 mm) circumference and 20 ft (6·1 m) in length. The running end is to be fitted with a 3-in (76 mm) swivel-type snap hook, and at the other end is to be fitted a small hook for attaching the line to the harness of a breathing apparatus set. (As guide lines now have directional markings, there is no need for the larger hook to be serrated.) A 'D' ring is to be fitted to the line 4 ft (1·22 m) from the running end to allow the use of a 'short' line when a guide line is being followed. Personal lines are described and illustrated in Book 2 of the *Manual*, Chapter 11. The line is to be carried in a suitable pouch attached to the harness of the breathing apparatus set.

4 Procedure for the use of guide and personal lines

(1) A guide line team should consist of a minimum of two men.

(2) The guide line is to be carried by the team leader. The last man of the team is to make the line fast at suitable points at a convenient height from the ground. Tie-off points need not be close together but at sufficient intervals to keep the line off the ground.

(3) The line is to be made fast on the side of search, and crossing over from one side to the other is to be avoided as far as possible.

(4) When it is known or suspected that the penetration will be deep, an additional guide line should be carried by another member of the team.

(5) When a guide line is being laid, members of the team other than the leader should attach themselves to the line by means of the hook of their personal line, so arranged to use the short (4 ft) (1·22 m) length of line. Alternatively, the members may attach themselves to the man in front instead of to the guide line (Fig. 12.2).

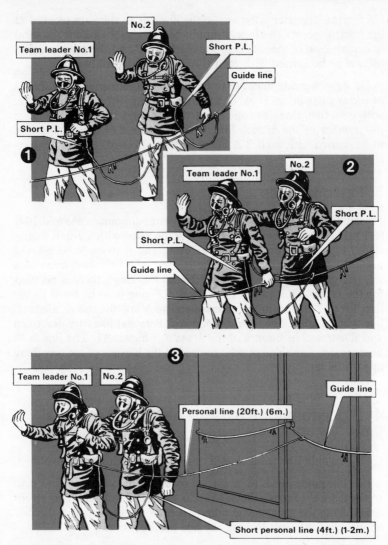

Fig. 12.2 (1) A method of following a guide line by each man attaching his short personal line to the guide line. (2) An alternative method by linking to the man in front. (3) Searching off a guide line to the full extent of the personal line

(6) After a guide line has been laid, all members of teams proceeding along the route are to attach themselves to the line by means of their short personal line. Alternatively, the leader will attach himself to the guide line and the remaining members may attach themselves to the man in front instead of to the guide line.

(7) When attached individually to the guide line by means of their short personal line, team and crew members should maintain contact so far as possible by physical touch.

(8) If a team laying a guide line has to retire before the objective is reached, the container and line should be removed and made fast at a convenient point for subsequent use by reliefs.

(9) To search off or otherwise move away from a guide line, personal lines should be used up to the limit of their length, i.e. 20 ft (6·1 m). Where the distance is greater than can be covered with one personal line, a branch guide line must be used.

(10) Designating tallies affixed to guide lines must not be removed except on the instructions of the B A Control Officer.

(11) For difficult jobs, reconnaissance and in other cases where the officer-in-charge directs, the first team to enter a building may be a 'communications team' (*see* Chapter 11, 'Communications Procedure'). In such cases the communications cable should be secured at intervals above ground level so far as is practicable.

(12) Where circumstances require a guide line to be laid following a communications cable, the team should clip on to the cable. The guide line should preferably not be made fast at the same points as the communications cable.

(13) A communications cable is not to be used as a guide line except under the circumstances described in paragraph (12) above, or by communications teams withdrawing after laying a cable and relief teams entering to connect on to a cable laid by a previous team.

(14) It is not necessary for men manning branches to remain attached to the guide line by means of the personal line.

(15) Outgoing teams should always have precedence on the guide line over ingoing teams.

5 Notes on the guide and personal line procedure

a. Guide lines

It will be seen that guide lines are used only on the instructions of the officer-in-charge; that only one main guide line may be laid along a route and that not more than two main guide lines are to originate from one B A Control. A maximum of four branch lines may be used from each B A Control. If operated to the maximum, the diagrammatic layout of guide lines from one B A Control could be as shown in Fig. 12.3. It will be the responsibility of the B A Control Officer to record the details of guide lines and the teams and crews working with them on the B A Stage II control board.

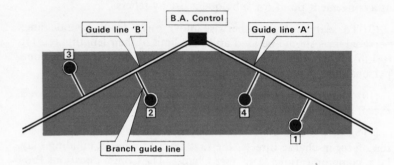

Fig. 12.3 Diagrammatic layout showing how two main guide lines and four branch lines could be laid from a B A Control

It should be noted that the laying of branch lines from main guide lines may not necessarily be in consecutive order. When it is decided to use branch lines they are given the numerical tallies starting from '1', and it is not possible to determine in advance where and when a branch line may be required, as this will depend on conditions inside the building and will not be known until after teams have got to work initially. For example, in Fig. 12.3 the first branch line has been laid from main guide line 'A', the second and third branch lines from main guide line 'B' and the last branch line from main guide line 'A'.

When reliefs are to be sent in, it is important that they relieve the right team, and B A Control Officers must ensure that crews are correctly instructed as to which main or branch line they are to follow. The men themselves must ensure that they find the correct guide line.

b. Personal lines

Provision is made for each breathing apparatus to have a personal line secured to it so that the man wearing the set may attach himself to a guide line. The personal line may be used to its full extent (20 ft (6·1 m)) when searching off a guide line (Fig. 12.2 (3)), or it may be used 'short' (4 ft (1·22 m)) for traversing a guide line (Fig. 12.2 (1) and (2)).

There are two methods of using the personal line when traversing a guide line:

(1) for each member of the team to attach himself to the guide line (Fig. 12.2 (1)), or alternatively,

(2) for the leader to attach himself to the guide line, and the following members of the team to attach themselves in a line one to another (Fig. 12.2 (2)) by means of their short personal line.

Method (2) has the advantage that when crews pass each other along the guide line when entering or leaving, it is only necessary for the team leader to unhook himself from the guide line and then re-engage his hook, instead of each member of the crew having to disengage and re-engage separately. Method (2) is also particularly useful when conditions are known to be without structural hazards, i.e. on level ground, but care must be exercised where openings and stairways are likely to be encountered. Vertical ladders, as, for example, on ships, make it difficult for method (2) to be used.

Chapter 13
The use of air-line equipment for fire fighting

Air-line equipment has been designed to extend the period of time of working with compressed-air breathing apparatus, and also to allow men to work with greater facility in confined spaces, such as reaching an incident in a ship's propeller shaft tunnel. The equipment basically comprises a breathing apparatus face mask supplied by air from cylinders situated outside the building or hazard (*see* page 74). The men are thus free of the weight and encumbrance of full breathing apparatus, although the trailing air-line may present a problem if the men have to penetrate any great distance into a hazard, or negotiate bends or stairways. Air-line equipment, however, is not a substitute for breathing apparatus under normal conditions.

The Central Fire Brigades Advisory Council have considered the use of air-line equipment for fire fighting and have made the following recommendations regarding the conditions under which this equipment should be used and the precautionary measures which should be taken.

1 Conditions of use

This equipment should be used only under the following conditions:

a. With compressed-air breathing apparatus

In known conditions (i.e. where the size, layout and contents of premises are known) for the purpose of extending the working duration where operational conditions permit. In these circumstances the breathing apparatus cylinder should be held in reserve for use in a possible emergency.

b. Without breathing apparatus

(1) When men are working in sight of a supervisory officer and it is desirable to have a longer duration than that provided by a compressed-air breathing apparatus; and,

(2) When breathing apparatus is too bulky for wear for a particular task.

2 Other requirements

(a) In all these circumstances, it is considered that the maximum length of air line should not exceed 300 ft (91 m), although normally it will probably not be possible to penetrate more than 200 ft (61 m) because of the drag of the hose and the resistance caused by the hose round bends *en route*. It must also be remembered that, whereas in an emergency a man wearing breathing apparatus can uncouple the air line and withdraw using the cylinder on his set, men not wearing breathing apparatus will be impeded in their withdrawal by having to make up the hose on their way out.

(b) The standard 'Breathing Apparatus Procedure' should be observed. To this end a distress signal warning device and tally should be provided for each mask supplied with air-line equipment when breathing apparatus is not worn. These tallies should have permanently entered on them AIR LINE where cylinder pressure is normally recorded and it is considered that standard compressed-air breathing apparatus tallies will be perfectly suitable for this purpose.

(c) When breathing apparatus is worn, the masks supplied for use with the air line, together with their associated distress signal warning devices and tallies, should be removed and left at the B A Control. The tally for the breathing apparatus should be used with the cylinder pressure and 'time in' recorded in the normal way; AIR LINE should be entered on the control board in the '*time of whistle*' column and 'WITH B A' entered in the '*Remarks*' column. The tallies with the air-line masks should be used when breathing apparatus is not worn. The '*time in*' should be noted and AIR LINE should be recorded in the '*time of whistle*' column on the control board.

(d) Men should work in pairs, both being supplied by one air line terminating in a 'Y' piece attached to the belt or harness of the second man (*see* Fig. 5.19). One branch of the 'Y' is connected to the mask of the second man and the other branch to the leading man by a hose not more than 10 ft (3 m) in length.

(e) Men standing by at a B A Control for emergency purposes should wear breathing apparatus unless the men at work are wearing air-line equipment because breathing apparatus is too bulky for the task in hand, in which case the stand-by team should also wear air-line equipment.

3 Additional precautionary measures

(a) When breathing apparatus is not worn, men should wear a belt or harness to which the air line is made fast, to prevent a drag on the mask.

(b) One of the two men on an air line should have communication equipment to enable him to be in constant touch with the B A Control Officer.

(c) When breathing apparatus is worn, a man must never disconnect his air line except in an emergency to allow a quick withdrawal.

(d) The air supply cylinders should be under the supervision of a trained breathing apparatus operator responsible to the B A Control Officer. There should be at least 4500 litres of air immediately available (e.g. four 1240-litre cylinders, or two 2250-litre cylinders). There should be change-over facilities to enable a rapid switch from empty to fully-charged cylinders. Empty cylinders should be replaced immediately by full ones.

(e) The air supply from the cylinders should pass through a reducing valve, which should be pre-set to the required working pressure, i.e. it should not be capable of adjustment without tools. The supply line on the cradle should also incorporate a low-cylinder-pressure warning whistle. A three-minute warning would be adequate as the change-over from empty to full cylinders can be achieved almost instantaneously, and in any case the contents of the air line provide an appreciable reserve of air.

(f) The air-line hose should be $\frac{1}{4}$-in (6 mm) internal diameter, be suitable for a maximum working pressure of 150 lbf/in² (10 bars) and be carried on a reel. The hose must be resistant to heat to the extent that it will comply with the following test:

'A length of the hose is to be subjected to the normal working pressure, e.g. about 100 lbf/in² (7 bars). A section of at least 3 ins (76 mm) in length is to be held in contact with a plate maintained at a temperature of 130°C for a period of 15 minutes during which time there must be no sign of failure.'

Chapter 14
Working in pressurised atmospheres

1 Historical

In 1966 a Home Office Technical Bulletin (No. 7/1966) was issued describing the effects of working in pressurised atmospheres when wearing breathing apparatus. Since that date new information has come to light as a result of a series of trials, and so it was decided that changes should be made to the recommended maximum pressure at which oxygen breathing apparatus may be worn, and in other factors. Accordingly, Technical Bulletin 7/1966 was cancelled and replaced by a new Technical Bulletin, No. 1/1972.

One of the recommendations in Technical Bulletin 7/1966 was that *Proto* breathing apparatus could be worn at pressures up to 18 lbf/in² (1·2 bars). This figure was based on practical experience with these sets as at that time no research work had been carried out on men breathing oxygen when performing hard work in air under pressure, although a great deal was known of the effects of breathing oxygen under water. A series of trials was therefore undertaken by the Royal Naval Physiological Laboratory with the co-operation of about 40 volunteers from Portsmouth Fire Brigade wearing *Proto* breathing apparatus. These trials were conducted under strict medical supervision and entailed the men carrying out a prescribed pattern of work for a set period at pressures ranging from 9 to 21 lbf/in² (0·6 to 1·4 bars) gauge.

The results of these tests indicated that the pressure of 18 lbf/in² (1·2 bars) gauge recommended in Technical Bulletin 7/1966 was too near the limit of safety, bearing in mind the extreme variability in the sensitivity of oxygen of different individuals. This could have been corrected by reducing the maximum pressure for oxygen sets by, say, 2 to 16 lbf/in² (0·1 to 1·1 bars) gauge; but the tests also revealed that despite the normal clearance procedure being followed when the sets were donned, the concentration of oxygen was generally very much lower than expected, in some cases as low as 70 per cent, the balance being nitrogen. This factor is important because the presence of nitrogen reduces the amount of oxygen to which the body is subjected and so increases the tolerance of the wearer to the effects of pressure; for example, breathing a mixture of 85 per cent oxygen and 15 per cent nitrogen at 18 lbf/in² (1·2 bars) gauge is equivalent to breathing pure oxygen at only 13 lbf/in² (0·9 bars) gauge. Therefore, although a pressure of 16 lbf/in² (1·1 bars) gauge might be acceptable for *Proto* breathing apparatus in view of the lower oxygen concentration in the breathing mixture, it would be too high in the case of other sets such as the *Minox* ni which the oxygen concentration would be very much higher.

Accordingly it has been decided that the pressure limit for the use of oxygen breathing apparatus should be adjusted to allow a wearer to breathe pure oxygen with an adequate safety margin and be reduced to 12 lbf/in^2 (0·8 bars) gauge pressure.

In addition to this question of the pressure limit for the use of oxygen sets, other developments have occurred since Technical Bulletin 7/1966 was issued. Revised tables providing longer decompression times than the tables in 'The Work in Compressed-Air Special Regulations 1958' are being tried out experimentally on the recommendations of a sub-committee of the Medical Research Council. In addition, more is known about the effects of oxygen poisoning and the question of mixture breathing apparatus for use at pressures above that recommended for oxygen breathing apparatus has been explored.

2 General considerations

a. Introduction

It is sometimes necessary to work under artificially pressurised conditions, e.g. when building a tunnel under a river, pressure may have to be increased to prevent the ingress of water. Regulations made under the Factories Act entitled 'The Work in Compressed-Air Special Regulations 1958' (Statutory Instrument No. 61) lay down requirements and precautions to be taken when work is undertaken in such conditions. There has to be an air lock at the entry to the workings to prevent the escape of compressed air. The Regulations state that there shall be a lock attendant and that pressure gauges shall be provided to indicate the pressure in the workings and the pressure in the air lock. The lock attendant controls the pressure in the air lock to compress men gradually before entering the workings and to decompress them on leaving. Decompression must be carried out in accordance with tables included in the Regulations.

When being pressurised it is necessary from time to time to hold the nose and 'blow' with the mouth closed in order to clear the ears. A man with a cold, ear-ache or sore throat, or who is suffering from bronchial or catarrhal trouble, should not be pressurised. In the event of a man feeling pain or discomfort while being pressurised, he should warn the lock attendant, who will stop compression and, if the pain does not go, will reduce pressure slowly and let the man out of the lock.

b. Pressure scales

As is well known the pressure of the atmosphere on the earth's surface is about $15\,lbf/in^2$ (say, 1 bar). Zero on this scale, which is known as the 'absolute' scale, would be found only in a perfect vacuum. Pressure gauges, on the other hand, are scaled to read zero at atmospheric pressure, so that 2 atmospheres or $30\,lbf/in^2$ (2 bars) absolute is equal to $15\,lbf/in^2$ (1 bar) gauge pressure. In other words, absolute pressure is always $15\,lbf/in^2$ (1 bar) more than the equivalent gauge pressure. When referring to pressures, therefore, it is important to specify whether the figures referred to are 'absolute' or 'gauge' readings. In this chapter, all pressures mentioned subsequently are gauge presssures as this is the scale used throughout 'The Work in Compressed-Air Special Regulations 1958'.

c. The effects of increased pressure

It is generally known that if a certain volume of gas at atmospheric pressure (zero gauge) is compressed by doubling the pressure to $15\,lbf/in^2$ (1 bar), then the volume is reduced to a half; if the pressure is increased by three times, i.e. $30\,lbf/in^2$ (2 bars), the volume is reduced to one-third and so on.

If a man enters an atmosphere of, say, $15\,lbf/in^2$ (1 bar) he will inhale the same volume of air at each breath as under atmospheric conditions, but this will, in fact, contain twice the amount of air as compared with air at atmospheric pressure. Another effect of entering an atmosphere of $15\,lbf/in^2$ (1 bar) is that gases dissolved in the body will increase and will eventually be double the amount of gases dissolved at atmospheric pressure. This change occurs without any discomfort to the man provided the increase in pressure is not too sudden and presents no problem until he returns to atmospheric conditions when the pressurised gases in the body expand and seek to escape.

d. Releasing pressurised gases in the body

When a man returns to atmospheric conditions from a pressurised atmosphere the extra gases dissolved in the body have to be released. The problem when breathing air under pressure arises from the increase in nitrogen in the body. When a man returns to atmosphere, this extra gas has to be expelled by being breathed out through the lungs. This occurs quickly in the case of a man who has not been exposed to pressures above $18\,lbf/in^2$ (1·2 bars), but at higher pressures a man needs to be decompressed at a controlled rate as, if the pressure is reduced too quickly and the nitrogen tries to get free faster than is possible through the lungs, bubbles of nitrogen will form in the body causing symptoms such as pain, particularly in the joints (when it is referred to as the 'bends'). These symptoms could be more severe after prolonged exposure, i.e. 3 hours or more to high pressure, and are known as 'decompression sickness'. The cure is to increase the pressure so that the gases are once more dissolved in the body and to decompress at the appropriate rate.

e. Decompression rates

The Regulations state that at pressures up to 18 lbf/in² (1·2 bars), there is no limit to the permissible working period and no special decompression measures are necessary. For pressures above 18 lbf/in² (1·2 bars), however, minimum times to decompress are given in the decompression tables according to the pressure to which the man has been subjected and the length of time he has been at work. The following extract from these tables (Table 4) shows how the time to decompress increases as the pressure increases up to 30 lbf/in² (2 bars) for working periods up to 1 hour.

Table 4

Pressure lbf/in²	Bars	Working period	Minimum time to decompress
18–20	1·2–1·4	½ to 1 hour	4 minutes
20–22	1·4–1·5	do.	6 do.
22–24	1·5–1·7	do.	8 do.
24–26	1·7–1·8	do.	10 do.
26–28	1·8–1·9	do.	13 do.
28–30	1·9–2·0	do.	16 do.

As already stated, the decompression tables referred to above are included in the Regulations, but a special panel of the Medical Research Council known as the 'Decompression Sickness Panel' has been studying the effect of decompression and has produced an alternative set of tables. These tables are known as the 'Blackpool Decompression Tables' and a number of contractors have received special dispensation to use them on an experimental basis. The Blackpool tables start controlled decompression at 14 lbf/in² (0·9 bar) instead of 18 lbf/in² (1·2 bars) and their general effect is to reduce decompression times between 18 and 30 lbf/in² (1·2 to 2 bars) pressure and to increase them at higher pressures. Table 5 shows the Blackpool figures up to 30 lbf/in² (2 bars) and the difference will be noted between these figures and those in Table 4.

3 The effects of wearing breathing apparatus

When a man enters a pressurised atmosphere wearing breathing apparatus, whether it be a compressed-air or oxygen set, his body

Table 5

Pressure lbf/in²	Bars	Working period	Minimum time to decompress
14–16	0·9–1·1	½–1 hour	2 minutes
16–18	1·1–1·2	do.	2 do.
18–20	1·2–1·4	do.	2 do.
20–22	1·4–1·5	do.	2 do.
22–24	1·5–1·7	do.	5 do.
24–26	1·7–1·8	do.	5 do.
26–28	1·8–1·9	do.	10 do.
28–30	1·9–2·0	do.	15 do.

is subjected to the same pressure both inside and out as if he were not wearing a set. The internal pressure builds up automatically to balance the external pressure; in the case of a compressed-air set at the exhaling valve and the diaphragm controlling the demand valve, and in the case of an oxygen set in the breathing bag. Different problems, however, arise according to whether air or oxygen is breathed and these are considered separately in the following paragraphs.

a. Compressed-air breathing apparatus

As regards effects on the body and the decompression measures to be taken on leaving the pressurised atmosphere, the same conditions apply as if no set were worn. An operational problem arises, however, from the fact that a man in a pressure of, say, 15 lbf/in² (2 atmospheres) inhales twice the amount of air he would inhale at atmospheric pressure, and consequently the nominal duration of the set is halved. At 30 lbf/in² (3 atmospheres) the duration would be reduced to one-third and so on, and it should also be noted that the safety margin indicated by the low-cylinder-pressure warning whistle would be reduced in the same ratio as the working duration of the set. These reductions in duration obviously impose severe limitations on the use of compressed-air sets, particularly at high pressures, unless special provision can be made to maintain the supply of air cylinders or air from another source (e.g. by means of air-line equipment).

b. Oxygen breathing apparatus

When oxygen at a high concentration is breathed in atmospheric or pressurised conditions, the nitrogen dissolved in the body will gradually be replaced by oxygen, the nitrogen being breathed out into the set and to some extent expelled through the relief valve. This transfer takes place without any ill effects and as oxygen can readily be used up in the body in a very short space of time there is no need for a controlled decompression on return to atmosphere. If, however, oxygen is breathed above a certain pressure, danger can arise from a phenomenon known as 'oxygen poisoning', and to understand this it is necessary to give a simplified account of the function of oxygen in the body.

Normally oxygen in the body is held partly in solution but chiefly in the red blood cells in chemical combination. This chemical, known as *haemoglobin*, carries oxygen to the tissues, gives it up and in its place takes in carbon dioxide. Under normal atmospheric conditions, over 99 per cent of the oxygen needed by the body is carried in haemoglobin. When the atmospheric pressure is greatly increased, no more oxygen can be carried by the haemoglobin, but the amount of oxygen dissolved in the liquid part of the blood is increased. At high pressures enough oxygen is carried in solution for the needs of the body tissues and consequently no oxygen is given up by the haemoglobin. The effect of this is that the haemoglobin cannot pick up carbon dioxide which as a result accumulates in the tissue. This accumulation is dangerous. Too much oxygen in the body can by itself cause disturbance of the normal processes of metabolism and interfere with energy production. This hindrance is made worse by increased amounts of carbon dioxide, and the combination of the two is responsible for so-called oxygen poisoning. Oxygen poisoning therefore occurs more readily when a man is working hard because his body produces more carbon dioxide. The symptoms in many ways are similar to drunkenness and lead ultimately to unconsciousness.

The duration of *Proto* sets is reduced in pressurised atmospheres but, because these sets have a re-circulating system, the effect is less marked than in the case of compressed-air sets. It is not possible to state precise reductions in relation to the ambient pressure, but from experience gained during the Royal Naval Physiological Laboratory trials, it may be assumed that in an atmosphere of 12 lbf/in² (0·8 bars) the working duration of a 1-hour *Proto* set will be reduced by about 12 minutes, and the safety margin indicated by the warning whistle will be reduced in the same ratio. With *Minox* sets, however, the duration is only slightly affected by pressure because of the method of operation of the flow control unit.

It is safe to wear oxygen breathing apparatus at pressures up to 12 lbf/in² (0·8 bars) for the working duration of a nominal 1-hour set, i.e. about 45 minutes. Above that pressure, however, it is impossible to state safe working limits because toxic symptoms may occur sooner or later depending on the individual and the physical effort involved. It is for this reason, among others, that the use of mixture breathing apparatus has been investigated.

c. Masks with air-cushion seals

With air-cushion seals the pressure in the cushion must be the same as the ambient pressure. Therefore, when masks of this type are to be used under pressurised conditions the sealing plug to the cushion should be removed and replaced when the maximum pressure is reached.

4 Provision of special equipment

a. General

Underground workings vary in type and complexity. The tunnels and passageways for the Underground Railway at Oxford Circus are like a rabbit warren, whereas the tunnel under Southampton Water, built for the Central Electricity Generating Board to carry power cables, runs straight for its whole length of nearly 2 miles (3·2 km).

It is common, however, to all tunnels under construction that the 'going' under foot is somewhat hazardous; conditions are generally damp and sometimes misty. The cross-section of tunnels is usually circular, although some other shapes may be encountered, and as a circular tunnel is built and lined, beams are laid across at a convenient height to serve as sleepers for rails to carry the 'muck' trucks, usually referred to as 'skips'. Between the rails planks are laid to provide a footway especially for the men pushing the trucks, but these are laid in a casual fashion and there are often gaps between them. There is generally no other continuous footway and it is necessary to proceed carefully even in good visibility. In smoke, progress would inevitably be hazardous and slow.

The supply services fed into a tunnel under construction, whether pressurised or not, are electricity, water (about a 1-in (25 mm) bore pipe) and an air main (also about 1-in (25 mm) bore) if pneumatic boring equipment is used. Equipment may, however, be electrically operated, in which case no air main will be installed. The water main is for the purpose of supplying water to the working face, and arrangements may be made with the contractor for the provision of take-off points at intervals along its length to which standard hose reel tubing can be attached for fire-fighting purposes. Pneumatic equipment operates at 80–100 lbf/in² (5·5–7 bars) pressure and the air main may also have take-off points along its length.

For obvious reasons construction companies only pressurise workings when absolutely necessary. When a tunnel is to be pressurised, an air lock is installed at the beginning of the section. This usually consists of a steel chamber which is sealed into the tunnel with concrete which may be several feet (metres) thick, depending on the pressure it is intended to withstand. The electricity, water and air lines are embedded in the concrete and there would be no difficulty in making provision for additional supply lines, with suitable couplings at each end for delivery hose and air lines for breathing apparatus, and a conduit with wiring and connections at each end for breathing apparatus communications equipment, provided the necessary arrangements were made with the contractor before the air lock was installed. The water supply line for delivery hose may be extended along the tunnel and be provided with instantaneous outlets at intervals.

Often vertical shafts have to be sunk to the level at which a tunnel is to be driven and it may be necessary for a shaft to be pressurised, in which case an air lock is installed at the head of the shaft. These locks may only take one or two persons at a time and access to the foot of the shaft is by means of ladders and staging. As work progresses, the shaft air lock is usually replaced by an air lock in the tunnel. Provision may be made with the contractor for fire brigade supply lines through these locks in the same way as for locks in tunnels.

Before a decision can be reached on the supplies to be installed through an air lock, it is necessary for the brigade to decide what would be the most suitable equipment to use in the event of an incident in that particular section of the workings. The choice of equipment should be based on the highest pressure the contractor thinks he may have to use. This maximum may never be reached as the pressure is kept as low as practicable, but it may have to be increased as tunnelling progresses.

b. Types of breathing apparatus

Oxygen sets would be the obvious choice as their duration is only moderately affected by the increased pressure and they allow wearers complete freedom of movement. However, if the pressure is above that recommended for the use of oxygen sets, then provision must be made for the use of compressed-air or special breathing apparatus (*see* paragraph (**e**) below).

With pressures over 12 lbf/in^2 (0·8 bars) even the ultra-lightweight cylinders are unlikely to provide an adequate working duration for a compressed-air set, and it will be necessary to augment the supply of air carried in the cylinders. This can be done either by making available sufficient spare cylinders or by using air-line equipment. Each of these methods has its own particular problems, and these are discussed in the following paragraphs.

c. Spare cylinders

Taking in sufficient spare cylinders creates a serious transporting problem under very difficult conditions. One possibility would be to make use of an empty skip to carry the cylinders, but there would be the likelihood of encountering another skip, perhaps fully loaded, or some other obstruction on the line which would prevent further progress. In the tunnel under Southampton Water, there were two overhead trolly tracks running the full length. These would provide a ready means for transporting equipment, but tracks of this type in tunnels are exceptional and would probably only be installed where cables or pipes had to be laid after the tunnel was completed. In some large tunnels battery-driven locomotives are used to move the skips and these would simplify the problems of transport.

It would therefore be reasonable to consider providing sufficient reserves of air in spare cylinders only if the means of transporting them were known to be reliable. However, where an adequate supply of spare cylinders could be made available, the breathing apparatus should be provided with two-way adaptors to enable cylinders to be replaced during operations. Alternatively, special arrangements could be made for a man to carry a spare cylinder already connected to his set.

d. Air-line equipment

When air-line equipment is used, the transporting of supply cylinders should not present serious difficulties if provision has been made for a special air line through the air lock for fire brigade use, which would permit the supply of cylinders to remain outside the lock. In such a case firemen could enter the pressurised section breathing air from the cylinder on their breathing apparatus and carrying a reel of air-line hose, which they could then plug into the special air line inside the pressurised section and connect to their sets, keeping in reserve the air remaining in the cylinders they are carrying. Penetration of the tunnel could then proceed up to the length of hose on a reel which is at most 300 ft (91 m). A transporting problem, however, arises if deeper penetration were necessary as a spare reel would have to be brought in to extend the line. Transporting a reel this distance would present difficulties, bearing in mind the condition of the timber staging and obstructions in tunnels under construction, and the heavy drain on the air in the breathing apparatus cylinders of sets worn by the men undertaking the work. If reliable transport facilities were available, it might be a practical proposition, and it might even be possible to transport both supply cylinders and air lines into the tunnel to a point convenient for operations.

An alternative would be to make use of the air main where one is installed for pneumatic tools. In such cases the air is supplied by large compressors, usually on the surface, and the use of this main would have the advantage of providing a continuous supply of air for an indefinite period, dispensing with the need to arrange for a supply of air from cylinders. The air from the main would have to be dried and freedom from oil mist ensured to make it suitable for breathing. This type of air installation may be found to have a high water content, in which case it will be necessary to allow time to drain the system to expel any accumulation of water before coupling up. In order to dry the air sufficiently to allow comfortable breathing, a special filter unit should be incorporated in the feed from the main to the air-line hose reel. The filter units can be obtained from the suppliers of air-line equipment.

Whenever air-line equipment is used the limiting factor will be the duration of the sets worn by the men which they will use on entering until the air line is connected up and subsequently on withdrawal after the air line is disconnected. Bearing in mind the limited duration of these sets under pressure and the difficulties involved, it is not considered likely that it will be practicable to penetrate a toxic atmosphere in excess of 300 ft (91 m), i.e. one hose reel length.

e. Special breathing apparatus

At pressures above 12 lbf/in² (0·8 bars), when oxygen breathing apparatus should not be worn, there are likely to be circumstances where the limitations on the duration of compressed-air sets and the restrictions imposed by air-line equipment would seriously hamper operations. Consideration has therefore been given to special breathing apparatus which would provide a working duration of at least 45 minutes irrespective of the pressure in which it is used, and which would be self-contained, consequently allowing complete freedom of movement to the wearer.

In order to avoid oxygen poisoning it is necessary for the oxygen breathed to be diluted with an inert gas, usually nitrogen, and the amount of dilution will depend on the pressure in which the set is to be used. A liquid air set would provide this gas mixture. These sets have the advantage of providing cool air for long periods, but it is not considered that the provision of these sets could be justified to meet a remote contingency, particularly in view of the high cost of the apparatus and the difficulty of keeping a supply of liquid air constantly available. A practical alternative, however, is to convert *Proto* 1-hour sets to 'mixture' breathing apparatus as used by the Royal Navy and to use a 60 per cent oxygen and 40 per cent nitrogen mixture. This is a standard Navy mixture which permits a man to work hard with no ill effects for periods up to 1 hour in pressures up to 35 lbf/in² (2·4 bars) irrespective of the degree of work undertaken by the wearer.

The conversion of *Proto* sets entails the provision of a 2-hour *Proto* cylinder, a special reducing valve giving a rate of flow of 6 litres per minute and the fitting of an automatic relief valve. A 2-hour Protosorb charge must be used and the set should be fitted with Mark V breathing tubes because they provide a lower breathing resistance than Mark IV tubes. The warning period indicated by the low-cylinder-pressure warning whistle will not be affected because the larger cylinder compensates for the effects of pressure. The cylinders can be charged commercially, and will be painted grey and black with the percentages of oxygen and nitrogen stencilled on them.

Firemen likely to wear mixture breathing apparatus should receive special instruction in their maintenance and use. Mixture sets behave differently from standard *Proto* sets in that, with a constant flow of 6 litres per minute, the relief valve is venting continuously and the set is under slightly higher internal pressure. Good maintenance is essential and it is important that the flow never drops below 5·7 litres per minute. If the flow drops below this figure or the reducing valve should fail, the bag will continue to remain full for some time and the wearer might be unaware of the fact that he is steadily reducing the oxygen content. This could be dangerous because lack of oxygen causes a man to behave as if drunk and eventually lose consciousness. Men working in pairs should bear this in mind when watching their companions.

With proper maintenance, a reducing valve is unlikely to become defective, but even so it is essential that firemen withdraw promptly at the limit of their working duration or if they have any reason to suspect the functioning of the reducing valve.

The duration tables for 1-hour *Proto* sets are applicable to these mixture breathing apparatus as the working durations of both sets are approximately the same. White tallies should be provided for mixture sets, marked at each end and in the centre with a $\frac{1}{4}$-in (6 mm) wide grey band to distinguish mixture sets from 1-hour *Proto* sets.

It is essential that the entrapped procedure is not practised with mixture breathing apparatus. The reason for this is that, because of the high nitrogen content, the breathing bag will not show signs of deflating before the wearer is breathing an excessive amount of nitrogen, which can have serious consequences.

5 Time of withdrawal

Attention has been drawn to the fact that the operation of low-cylinder-pressure warning whistles on some sets is affected by pressure and will give a reduced warning period. Whatever apparatus is used, it is essential to start withdrawal in sufficient time to allow for possible delay in entering the air lock, which may be in use at the time of the wearer's return, and in view of the need to allow this extra safety margin it would in any case not be practicable to rely on low-cylinder-pressure warning whistles.

6 Summary

The choice of breathing equipment to use in pressurised workings depends on the pressure, the ease of access to the workings and also on the arrangements it is possible to make with the contractor before an air lock is installed. The conditions may be split into two groups:

(a) where pressures are low enough to permit the breathing of pure oxygen, and (b) where pressures are too high for pure oxygen to be breathed.

a. Lower pressures

It is not always most convenient to use self-contained breathing apparatus and at pressures up to 12 lbf/in² (0·8 bars) oxygen sets are to be preferred because they provide the longer duration which is not materially affected by the pressure. Compressed-air sets may be used if their duration is considered to be sufficient in the prevailing circumstances.

b. Higher pressures

At higher pressures where pure oxygen should not be breathed, there are three possible alternatives:

(1) Where penetration is not deep and transporting facilities are known to be reliable

Self-contained compressed-air breathing apparatus could be used with a supply of sufficient spare cylinders to last the required working duration. Sets used for this purpose would require a special adaptor to allow a full cylinder to be fitted while the one to be replaced was still in use.

(2) Where the depth of penetration is too deep for (1) above

Air-line equipment could be used in conjunction with self-contained compressed-air breathing apparatus. The cylinder on the set should be used until the air-line reel is connected up and then the cylinder should be shut off and kept in reserve. Where reliable transport facilities exist within the workings, large capacity air supply cylinders and air lines could be taken into the pressurised section to a point convenient for operations.

(3) Special breathing apparatus

Sets of this type may be provided in a brigade by converting standard *Proto* 1-hour breathing apparatus. These sets have the advantage of being self-contained and of being safe to use in pressures up to 35 lbf/in² (2·4 bars) for the working duration of the apparatus, i.e. at least 45 minutes.

In all cases ample time should be allowed for withdrawal, bearing in mind that there may be a delay at the air lock. Reliance should not be placed on low-cylinder-pressure warning whistles.

Part 3
Resuscitation

No attempt is made in this Part to give a comprehensive treatise on the subject of resuscitation, but only to give a general summary of what a fireman should know and what equipment is available to him, in order that he can give emergency treatment until doctors or other qualified persons, such as ambulancemen, become available.

The Joint Training Committee of the Central Fire Brigades Advisory Council has made recommendations on first-aid training generally, and most fire brigade personnel receive instruction based on *First Aid*, the authorised manual of the St John Ambulance Association and Brigade, the St Andrew's Ambulance Association and the British Red Cross. The Committee also recommended that continuation training should be based on the booklet *Digest of First Aid*, which is also published by the St John Ambulance Association.

Chapter 15
Resuscitation

Until recent years, in cases when a person was unconscious and not breathing, various types of artificial respiration were applied and numerous lives were saved. However, in a number of instances these measures were unsuccessful because, although performed correctly, the heart had ceased to beat and so artificial respiration alone was not enough to prevent death. Now artificial respiration (mouth-to-mouth or mouth-to-nose) is combined with external cardiac compression so that more lives can be saved. The main object of external cardiac compression is to restart the heart, though, while it is being carried out, enough blood may be squeezed out of the heart to give rise to a pulse that can be felt. The combination of these two measures in an emergency—to restore breathing and heart action—is called *resuscitation*.

Anything which interferes with the intake and absorption of oxygen (respiration) produces asphyxia. If the lungs do not receive a sufficient supply of fresh air, important organs, especially the brain, are deprived of oxygen. If the brain is deprived of oxygen for 4 minutes, irreversible changes take place in it. The aim of respiratory resuscitation is the immediate oxygenation of the blood in order to forestall such changes. Although the person performing the mouth-to-mouth (or mouth-to-nose) method passes on to the casualty some air that he has used himself, there is enough oxygen in it (17 per cent compared with the 21 per cent in fresh air) to be effective. The urgent need for oxygenated blood is so great that only obvious obstructions should be removed before the lungs are inflated.

1 Oral and manual techniques

Resuscitation must be attempted in all cases of oxygen starvation where natural respiration has ceased, or has apparently ceased, including cases caused by suffocation (e.g. due to inhalation of smoke or oxygen deficient atmospheres generally), drowning, electric shock and strangulation.

The urgency of commencing some form of emergency resuscitation *immediately* cannot be over-emphasised. Unless this is done, neither the application of oxygen, the use of resuscitation apparatus, nor other attempts to revive the patient, are likely to prove successful. It is equally important to ensure an adequate airway to the patient's lungs during resuscitation. Nose and mouth must be cleared of any obstructions, and the tongue must not be allowed to fall back and block the windpipe.

A brief return to natural respiration should not be taken to mean that the need for resuscitation has ceased. Not infrequently the patient, after a temporary recovery of respiration, stops breathing again. The patient must, therefore, be watched and if natural breathing stops emergency resuscitation must be resumed at once.

Manual emergency resuscitation must be continued until respiration is restored or a doctor pronounces life to be extinct. Definite evidence of death, e.g. rigor mortis, should be insisted upon before attempts at emergency resuscitation are abandoned. There have been cases on record in which rescuers have persevered after life has been declared extinct and they have succeeded in saving the life of the patient. An unconscious person becomes cold very rapidly and this means an added strain on an already weakened vitality. The patient should, therefore, be kept covered whenever possible while efforts are being made to resuscitate him.

2 Methods of oral and manual resuscitation

The recommended method of oral resuscitation is mouth-to-mouth (or mouth-to-nose) and the manual methods recommended are Holger Nielsen and the Silvester. The oral method (Fig. 15.1) is

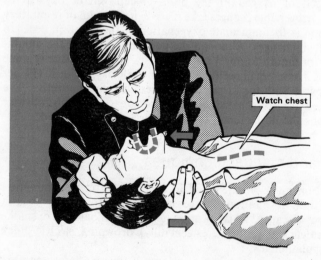

Fig. 15.1 The position for starting mouth-to-mouth resuscitation. The nape of the neck is supported, the head tilted backward and clothing is loosened at the neck and waist. The casualty's nostrils are pinched with the fingers, his mouth is sealed with the lips and his lungs inflated by blowing into his mouth. The rise and fall of the chest should be watched

preferred as it can be more easily applied than manual methods and can be used in some situations where they cannot; for example, in cases of drowning while the casualty is still in the water, or where an individual is trapped by a fall of earth and cannot be immediately released. Other advantages are:

(a) It gives the greatest ventilation of the lungs and oxygenation of the blood.

(b) The degree of inflation of the lungs can be assessed by watching the movement of the chest.

(c) It is less tiring, does not require strength and can be applied by a child.

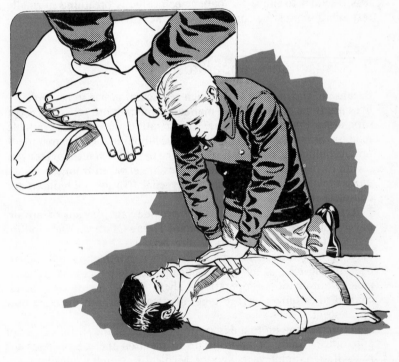

Fig. 15.2 External heart compression may be necessary if the heart is not beating. For adults, the hands are placed on the lower half of the breastbone, and with the arms kept straight, the breastbone is compressed about 60 times a minute with a rocking motion. Artificial respiration (not shown in the diagram) must be continued at the same time

If the heart is not beating, the casualty's colour remains or becomes blue/grey, his pupils are widely dilated when visible and the carotid pulse cannot be felt. If there is still cardiac arrest, then external cardiac compression (Fig. 15.2) may be necessary.

Difficulty in employing the oral method in cases of injury to the mouth or face and for other reasons is recognised. The alternative methods of manual resuscitation are the Holger Nielsen or the Silvester. Full descriptions of the techniques of these methods of manual resuscitation are given in *First Aid* and in *Digest of First Aid*.

Resuscitation should be carried out at the nearest possible point to where the patient is initially found. He should not normally be moved from this point until he is breathing naturally of his own accord, and then moved only in a prone position. If for any reason it is essential to move the patient before he is breathing normally, resuscitation must be continued while he is being moved.

3 Resuscitation apparatus

Because of the urgency with which resuscitation has to be applied if lives are to be saved, oral or manual techniques are generally necessary, at least in the early stages. Resuscitation apparatus, if available, relieves the rescuer of a great deal of the labour involved in manual or oral techniques and greatly increases the patient's chances of recovery owing to the fact that poisonous gases are expelled from the system more rapidly, and after-effects of oxygen starvation are reduced and complete recovery is accelerated.

Resuscitation apparatus usually provides air, oxygen or an air/oxygen mixture. There is no standard Home Office specification for resuscitation apparatus used by fire brigades, but the types which may be encountered are generally either extremely simple hand-operated devices, or fairly sophisticated resuscitators that are completely automatic in operation. There were one or two hand-controlled or lung-governed types of resuscitator, but these are now obsolescent.

Before passing on to a description of some of the various types of apparatus, it may be appropriate to mention the use of gases for resuscitation. Some years ago the Medical Research Council recommended that, in first-aid practice, pure oxygen and not a mixture of oxygen and carbon dioxide (carbogen) should be administered to persons suffering from respiratory failure or respiratory depression and requiring manual artificial respiration. The Council later gave further consideration to the question of first-aid treatment in cases of carbon monoxide poisoning, and recommended in such cases the use of 5 per cent of carbon dioxide in oxygen instead of pure oxygen; they confirmed, however, that pure oxygen should continue to be used for the treatment of asphyxia and anoxia.

So far as the fire service is concerned, it is often difficult in practical circumstances accurately to diagnose whether a casualty is suffering from carbon monoxide poisoning or respiratory failure from some other cause. There are obvious disadvantages in carrying two different cylinders for use with resuscitation apparatus. Most fire brigades now rely on cylinders of pure oxygen for resuscitation purposes.

Brief descriptions of examples of the different types of resuscitation apparatus are given in the following sections, but no attempt is made to give detailed working instructions nor the methods of testing and maintenance of the equipment. Reference should be made in all cases to the appropriate manufacturers' specifications and handbooks.

All persons likely to use resuscitation apparatus which uses oxygen should thoroughly appreciate and understand the dangers involved if grease or oil are allowed to come into contact with the equipment (see page 45). Failure to observe the necessary precautions may involve serious injury to either patient or operator, or both.

4 Hand-operated resuscitation apparatus

a. Air resuscitators

There are several types of hand-operated resuscitator available which deliver air to a face mask when a bellows or bag is compressed by the operator. One type which has been developed by the Ministry of Defence is the *Porton* positive pressure resuscitator (Fig. 15.3 (1)); another is the *Sabre airox* (Fig. 15.3 (2)).

When the bellows or bag is compressed, a non-return valve automatically ensures that air is forced through the mask connection to the patient. As soon as pressure is released, the bellows or bag expands and a fresh supply of air from the atmosphere is drawn in through an inlet valve. At the same time the non-return valve closes, ensuring that the air exhaled by the patient passes directly to the atmosphere.

Air resuscitators have the advantage over mouth-to-mouth (or mouth-to-nose) resuscitation in that they are hygienic and the air contains a higher percentage of oxygen than exhaled breath. Although a pressure relief valve is generally incorporated, care must be taken not to over-inflate the patient's lungs.

b. Air/oxygen resuscitators

Many of the hand-operated air resuscitators also have a connection so that they can be coupled to an oxygen supply to provide an air/oxygen mixture. One such type is the *Ambu* (Fig. 15.4 (1)); when resuscitation with an oxygen-enriched air is desirable, tubing from an oxygen cylinder can be attached to an oxygen inlet connection.

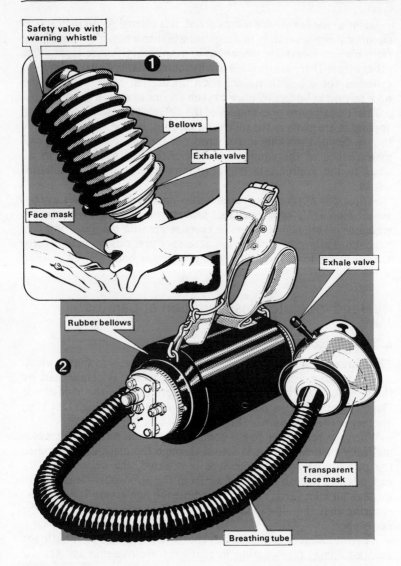

Fig. 15.3 Hand-operated air resuscitators. (1) The Porton positive pressure resuscitator. (2) The Sabre airox

A spring-loaded ball-type non-return valve in the tubing prevents air escaping from the bag when the oxygen supply is disconnected and the resuscitator is used to provide atmospheric air only.

Another type is marketed under the name of *Respirex ox-vital* or *Handyman* (Fig. 15.4 (2)). A feature of this resuscitator is that the

150

oxygen container is of special design; this takes the form of a coiled lightweight metal tube in which the oxygen is hermetically sealed under pressure to prevent leakage. The tube contains a 20-minute supply of oxygen which flows as soon as the seal is broken, there being no valves to manipulate or gauges to watch. The air/oxygen mixture contains 76–60 per cent of oxygen for the first 2 minutes, the percentage of oxygen gradually reducing to about 30–25 per cent

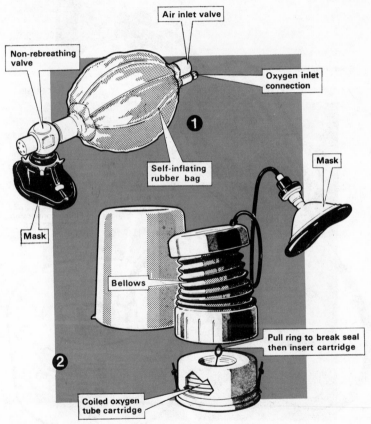

Fig. 15.4 Hand-operated air/oxygen resuscitators. (1) The Ambu resuscitator. (2) The Respirex ox-vital (or Handyman) resuscitator

during the last 5 minutes. If resuscitation has to be continued for longer than 20 minutes, a new oxygen cartridge can be fitted, or alternatively, continued operation with the bellows will provide atmospheric air without oxygen. The apparatus only weighs about 3 lb (1·36 kg) and is completely portable as it does not have to be connected to an external oxygen cylinder. The oxygen cartridge has to be returned to the manufacturers for recharging.

A larger version of this type of resuscitator is the *Respirex ball resuscitator*, or it is also sold under the name *Lifeman* (Fig. 15.5). The moulded transparent face mask enables the operator to see the

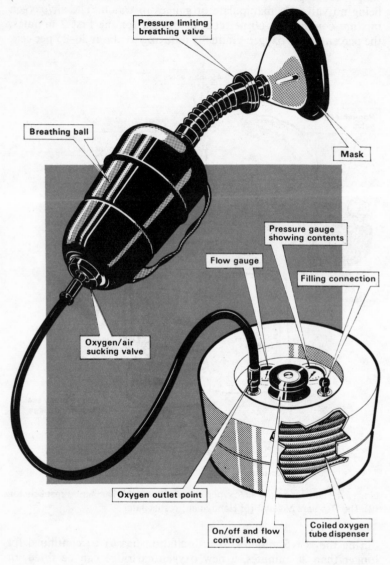

Pressure limiting breathing valve

Breathing ball

Mask

Pressure gauge showing contents

Flow gauge

Filling connection

Oxygen/air sucking valve

Oxygen outlet point

On/off and flow control knob

Coiled oxygen tube dispenser

Fig. 15.5 The Respirex ball resuscitator (or Lifeman) with oxygen dispenser

patient's mouth and nose and to verify that mucus is not blocking the airway; the pneumatic seal ensures an airtight fit. The mask is

152

attached to the breathing ball by a flexible tube. A double channel breathing valve prevents over-expansion of the lungs by limiting the inspired air/oxygen to the correct pressure. It also allows the air/oxygen mixture to pass into the face mask during the exhaling phase; this removes the exhaled air and thereby does away with the 'dead space'. The breathing ball incorporates an air/oxygen inlet valve; this mixes air with the oxygen to the required proportions. With each full compression of the breathing ball, the lungs are ventilated with a volume of 700/800 millilitres provided that the mask is firmly seated. The patient is also able to breathe spontaneously through the equipment.

An oxygen supply tube connects the breathing ball to the oxygen dispenser, which comprises the special coiled storage unit containing oxygen under pressure, a pressure gauge calibrated in atmospheres, a gauge which shows the rate of flow from 1 to 18 litres per minute, and a control setting handle for turning the oxygen on and off and setting the rate of flow. A connector is provided for recharging the oxygen storage unit. Some brigades who use this resuscitator have dispensed with the variable flow gauge and have had a reducing valve substituted; this is preset to allow a constant flow of about 4 litres per minute. The resuscitator is packed in an attache-type case, and the unit weighs about 17 lb (7·7 kg).

The main advantages of all these hand-operated resuscitators are that they are easy to operate—especially by comparatively untrained personnel—and that they obviate the need to apply oral or manual resuscitation.

5   Fully-automatic resuscitators

Automatic resuscitators provide artificial respiration on a positive pressure principle and supply oxygen or an air/oxygen mixture to the patient. With this type of apparatus both the inflation and deflation of the patient's lungs are automatically controlled by the resuscitator and so these sets can be used without the need for oral or manual artificial respiration. It should be emphasised, however, that manual or oral artificial respiration should always be commenced immediately until the apparatus is available and should be continued until the apparatus operator is ready to take over.

Several versions of fully-automatic resuscitators are available, but all operate on more or less similar principles. Essentially the apparatus consists of an oxygen cylinder (usually about 12 cubic feet (340 litres) capacity) to which is fitted a valve assembly consisting of a cylinder contents gauge and pressure-reducing valve regulators. These govern the flow of oxygen from the cylinder into the automatic timing or supply mechanism.

a. The Automan resuscitator

One type of fully-automatic resuscitator is the *Automan* (Fig. 15.6).
This operates on a timed cycle and adjusts itself automatically to the
lung capacity of the patient. Use of a timed cycle removes any of

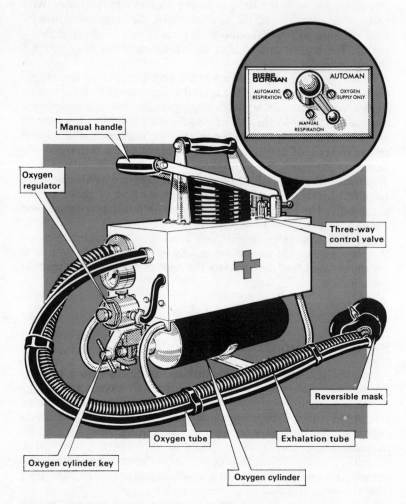

Fig. 15.6 The Automan fully-automatic resuscitation apparatus

the inherent dangers associated with a pressure-controlled cycle and
guards against the patient's lungs being over-inflated or remaining
inflated for an extended period.

A feature of this unit is that it may be used not only as an automatic resuscitator, but also as a hand-operated set, or as a constant flow oxygen therapy unit. The three alternative functions are facilitated by a three-way control valve located on the top of the unit. The manual resuscitator is designed for maintaining artificial respiration either while an oxygen cylinder is being changed, or in a remote location where a new oxygen cylinder is unavailable. An automatic relief valve set at 350 mm water gauge pressure prevents over-inflation of the patient's lungs.

When the valve is turned to 'automatic' the flow of oxygen is directed from the cylinder into the automatic timing mechanism. Oxygen passes from the timing unit along a narrow bore hose to a soft rubber anaesthetic mask. This mask is reversible, in two sizes, which are mounted back to back—one for adults and the other for small children and babies. The mask is linked to a corrugated rubber exhalation tube which terminates in a non-return valve fitted on the apparatus. A pressure gauge calibrated in minutes indicates the amount of oxygen left in the cylinder. The whole unit is mounted in a light metal carrying case mounted on sled runners, and weighs 27 lb (912·25 kg).

The apparatus automatically calculates the pressures, volumes and frequency of the breaths required by the patient without the use of any controls. Once the oxygen cylinder has been turned on, the apparatus measures the lung compliance of the patient and sets the mechanism to deliver the required tidal volume, minute volume frequency pressure and phasing needed by the patient. These factors are recalculated with each respiration and the resuscitator may be transferred from an adult to a child without any manual readjustment.

b. The Minuteman resuscitator

Another type of fully-automatic resuscitator is the *Minuteman* (Fig. 15.7). In this apparatus, the face mask is attached to a piece of apparatus known as a 'midget resuscitator' which is pressure sensitive, i.e. it cycles in response to positive and negative pressure built up in the patient's lungs. A rotatable ring round the body of the midget resuscitator enables the operator to vary the mixture of air and oxygen delivered to the patient, and the composition of the gas mixture determines the speed at which the resuscitator cycles. With the ring in the fully anti-clockwise position, a mixture of 50 per cent oxygen (including atmospheric oxygen) and 50 per cent atmospheric nitrogen is delivered and the maximum cycling speed is obtained. As the ring is rotated, the volume of air entrained by the oxygen stream is progressively reduced, thus increasing the oxygen percentage and reducing the cycling speed until, in the fully clockwise position, 100 per cent oxygen is delivered at the minimum cycling rate. The use of 100 per cent oxygen should not normally be used

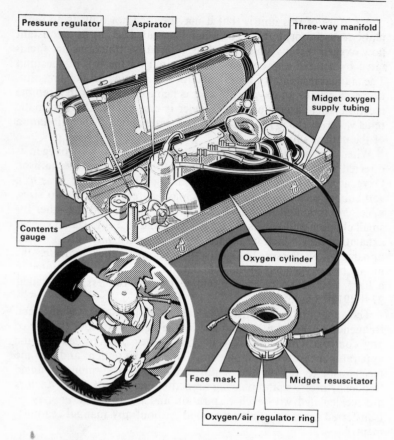

Pressure regulator

Aspirator

Three-way manifold

Midget oxygen supply tubing

Contents gauge

Oxygen cylinder

Face mask

Midget resuscitator

Oxygen/air regulator ring

Fig. 15.7 The Minuteman fully-automatic resuscitation apparatus

for more than 3 or 4 minutes at a time, as prolonged periods may result in respiratory acidosis. The mixture control should be returned to the 50 per cent oxygen position as soon as possible.

The selected mixture flows into the patient's lungs until the designed positive pressure is reached, when the direction of flow is automatically reversed, negative pressure assisting in the withdrawal of gases from the lungs. The exhaled gases are expelled through the expiratory port in the midget resuscitator until the designed negative pressure is reached, when the direction of flow is again reversed to start a new inspiratory phase.

An inspirator is also provided which may be used to clear the mouth, throat and nose of mucus or blood before resuscitation is started. Airway tubes in two different sizes (for adults and children) are for use when the patient is unconscious and not breathing, to prevent the tongue from falling back and closing the windpipe.

c. The Sabre Saturn or Star resuscitators

A third type of fully-automatic resuscitator is the *Sabre Saturn* or *Star* (the latter is a more comprehensively equipped version of the former, containing aspirator, airway tubes, etc.).

The main feature of this resuscitator is a *fluidic* valve (Fig. 15.8), which is an automatic resuscitation valve with manual over-ride and which has no moving parts. The inlet is supplied with oxygen or an oxygen/air mixture at a specific safe setting by means of a flow control unit. The flow meter is graduated in coloured settings and is the only control necessary.

The cycling action of the fluidic valve makes use of a 'wall attachment phenomenon' known as the 'Coanda' effect. The oxygen entering the valve at Fig. 15.8 (1) passes through the orifice (2). Because of the 'Coanda' effect, the oxygen is deflected along the wall X–Y and so enters the orinasal face mask of the resuscitator through channel (3) and outlet (4). The flow of oxygen into channel (3)

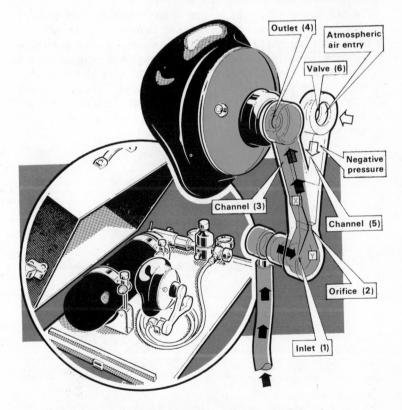

Fig. 15.8 The 'fluidic' resuscitation valve as fitted to the Sabre Saturn fully-automatic resuscitation apparatus

causes a slight negative pressure in channel (5) and atmospheric air under the effect of this negative pressure enters the valve at (6) and passes down channel (5) into channel (3), so mixing with the oxygen coming from (2). This phase of the cycle represents inflation of the lungs.

When the pressure in the mask, and therefore in channel (3), reaches a pre-determined pressure (according to the pressure of oxygen entering at (1)), the 'Coanda' effect is destroyed; the flow of oxygen coming from (2) is immediately diverted and enters channel (5), emerging at point (6). This creates a slight negative pressure in channel (3) and in the face mask, thus assisting the flow of exhaled air which the patient is breathing out. This represents the expiratory phase.

When the negative pressure in channel (3) and in the mask reaches approximately −20 mm of water column, the flow of oxygen coming through the orifice (2) no longer encounters pressure from channel (3) and will once again be deflected towards wall X–Y. The inhalation phase therefore automatically recommences.

The pressure at which the oxygen or oxygen/air mixture entering the fluidic valve equalises the pressure in channel (3) (and therefore in the patient's lungs) can be preset at a safe level and no control or adjustment is required. Alternatively, a gauge and manual control can be fitted which enables the operator to vary the maximum pressure in the patient's lungs between 50 and 200 mm of water column. An accessory shoe can be fitted over the vent (6) to prevent the ingress of toxic gas during the inhalation phase if the resuscitator is being used in a toxic atmosphere.

Manual of Firemanship:
Revised Structure

Book 1 Elements of combustion and extinction

Part	Part	Chapter	First published
1 Physics of combustion	1	1	1943
2 Chemistry of combustion	1	1	1943
3 Methods of extinguishing fire	1	2 and	1945
	6A	32(III)	1945

Book 2 Fire brigade equipment

Part	Part	Chapter	First published
1 Hose	1	4	1943
2 Hose fittings	1	5	1943
3 Ropes and lines, knots, slings, etc.	1	7 and	1943
	6A	39	1945
4 Small gear	1	13	1943

Book 3 Fire extinguishing equipment

Part	Part	Chapter	First published
1 Hand and stirrup pumps	1	8	1943
2 Portable chemical extinguishers	1	9	1943
3 Foam and foam-making equipment	1	10	1943

Book 4 Pumps and special appliances

Part	Part	Chapter	First published
1 Pumping appliances	2	1	1944
2 Practical pump operation	2	2	1944
3 Special appliances	2	6	1944

Book 5 Fire brigade ladders

Part	Part	Chapter	First published
1 Extension ladders	1	6	1943
2 Escapes and escape mountings	2	3	1944
3 Turntable ladders	2	4	1944
4 Hydraulic platforms	2	5	1944

Book 6 Breathing apparatus and resuscitation

Part	Part	Chapter	First published
1 Breathing apparatus	1	11	1943
2 Operational procedure	6A	32(V)	1945
3 Resuscitation	1	12	1943

Printed in England for Her Majesty's Stationery Office
by The Campfield Press, St. Albans

(2770) Dd 596088. K.40. 12/78. (T.S.100264)